Childcraft

GREAT MEN AND FAMOUS DEEDS

Childcraft

IN FIFTEEN VOLUMES

●

VOLUME SIX

GREAT MEN AND FAMOUS DEEDS

FIELD ENTERPRISES EDUCATIONAL CORPORATION
Merchandise Mart Plaza • **Chicago 54, Illinois**

1961 EDITION

CHILDCRAFT
(Reg. U.S. Pat. Off.)

CONTENTS

ADVENTURES OF FAMOUS PERSONS

MYTHS AND LEGENDS

ACKNOWLEDGMENTS

The publishers of CHILDCRAFT gratefully acknowledge the courtesy of the following publishers for permission to use the following copyrighted stories:

Abingdon Press: "Luther Burbank, Plant Magician," by Lillian J. Bragdon from *Luther Burbank, Nature's Helper,* copyright 1959; "Albert Schweitzer, Jungle Doctor" and "North to Labrador, a Story of Wilfred Grenfell" by May McNeer from *Armed with Courage,* copyright 1957.

Margaret Ford Allen: "When Mark Twain was a Boy" from *Child Life.*

Appleton-Century-Crofts, Inc.: "The Story of King Arthur" from *Mighty Men* by Eleanor Farjeon, copyright 1925, 1926 by Appleton, courtesy Eleanor Farjeon.

American Book Company: "The Story of William Tell" and "The Boy Lafayette, and the Wolf" from *Fifty Famous Stories* by James Baldwin; "Young George Washington," adapted from *Four Great Americans* by James Baldwin.

Thomas Hart Benton: "T.P. and Jake" from *Vineyard Gazette.*

Bobbs-Merrill Company: "The Chief at Warm Springs" from *Franklin Roosevelt: Boy of the Four Freedoms* by Ann Weil, copyright 1947; "The Story of Dolly Madison" from *Dolly Madison: Quaker Girl* by Helen A. Monsell, copyright 1944; "Abraham Lincoln's Boyhood" from *The Autobiography of Abraham Lincoln,* compiled by Nathaniel Wright Stephenson; "The Story of Jane Addams" from *Jane Addams: Little Lame Girl* by Jean Brown Wagoner, copyright 1944.

Thomas Y. Crowell Company: "Rosa Bonheur Breaks Her Needle" from *Stories of the Youth of Artists* by Mary Newlin Roberts; "Daniel Boone's New Home in Kentucky" from *On Indian Trails with Daniel Boone* by Enid LaMonte Meadowcroft.

J. M. Dent & Sons, Ltd.: "King of the Fur Traders" from *Pages from Canada's Story* by D. J. Dickie and Helen Palk, copyright 1929.

Dial Press, Inc.: "The Flight of Icarus" from *Stories of Gods and Heroes* by Sally Benson, copyright 1940 by Sally Benson.

Dodd, Mead & Company, Inc.: "Alexander Mackenzie" from *Knight of the Wilderness* by Maxine Shore and M. M. Oblinger, copyright 1943 by Dodd, Mead, courtesy McClelland & Stewart; "A New, Bright World for Jenny Lind" from *Enchanting Jenny Lind* by Laura Benét, copyright 1939.

Doubleday, Doran & Company, Inc.: "Pocahontas and Captain John Smith" from *Pocahontas* by Edgar and Ingri Parin d'Aulaire, copyright 1946.

Grosset and Dunlap, Inc.: "The Story of Madame Curie" by Alice Thorne, copyright 1959.

Houghton Mifflin Company: "Abraham Lincoln's Boyhood" in part from *The Real Lincoln* by J. W. Weik.

Alfred A. Knopf, Inc.: "Columbus Finds America" from *They Put Out to Sea* by Roger Duvoisin, copyright 1944 by Alfred A. Knopf, Inc., courtesy University of London Press.

Highlights for Children: "Louis Braille, the Boy Who Brought Light to the Blind," copyright 1960.

J. B. Lippincott Company: "Midas and the Golden Touch" from *Heroic Tales from Greek Mythology* by Katherine Pyle, copyright 1928, 1934; "John James Audubon" from *Tell Me a Birthday Story* by Carolyn Sherwin Bailey, copyright 1934, 1935; "Abraham Lincoln's Boyhood" in part from *The True Abraham Lincoln,* a book by William Eleroy Curtis.

Little, Brown & Company: "The Wright Brothers Learn to Fly" from *Heroes of Civilization* by Joseph Cottler and Haym Jaffe, copyright 1931 by Joseph Cottler and Haym Jaffe.

Lothrop, Lee & Shepard Company: "The True Story of Benjamin Franklin" from *The True Story of Benjamin Franklin* by Elbridge S. Brooks, copyright 1940.

Robert M. McBride & Company: "The Map That Came to Life" from *The Story Behind Great Books* by Elizabeth Rider Montgomery.

The Macmillan Company: "Abraham Lincoln's Boyhood" in part from *Life of Abraham Lincoln* by Ida Tarbell, copyright 1895, 1896, 1898, 1899 by S. S. McClure Company; 1900 by Doubleday & McClure Company and McClure Phillips & Company; 1917 by The Macmillan Company; 1924 by The Lincoln History Society.

McClelland and Stewart, Ltd.: "Alexander Graham Bell" from *Famous Canadian Stories,* edited by George E. Tait, copyright 1953.

Thomas Nelson & Sons, Ltd.: "The Feast of Eat-Everything" from *Canada's Story* by H. E. Marshall in Our Empire Story series, copyright 1932.

Julian Messner, Inc.: "Will Rogers: Immortal Cowboy" by Shannon Garst, copyright 1950.

G. P. Putnam's Sons: "Babe Ruth's Own Story" from *Babe Ruth's Own Book of Baseball* by George Herman Ruth.

Margaret I. Ross: "George Washington Carver" by Margaret I. Ross, from *Child Life.*

Charles Scribner's Sons: "Robert Fulton Makes the Paddles Work" from *The Boat Builder* by Clara Ingram Judson, copyright 1940; "Clara Barton, the Young Schoolteacher" from *Clara Barton* by Mildred Pace, copyright 1941.

Ruth Cromer Weir: "Teddy Roosevelt, the Boy Naturalist" by Ruth Cromer Weir.

The John C. Winston Company: "The Story of Robert E. Lee" from *Hero Tales from History* by Smith Burnham; "Robin Hood and Maid Marian" from *Robin Hood* by George Cockburn Harvey.

The Wisconsin Octopus: "Paul Bunyan's Christmas" by Taggert Ted Brown.

Wise, Winifred E.: "Thomas Alva Edison" from *Thomas Alva Edison, The Youth and His Times.*

ADVENTURES

OF FAMOUS PERSONS

Columbus Finds America

By Roger Duvoisin

ONE DAY there came into Lisbon, Portugal, a young Italian named Christopher Columbus. He was much interested in everything which had to do with the sea and ships, and he helped his brother Bartholomew to paint maps and sell books. He loved to watch the mariners unload from their sailing ships the monkeys, the bright parrots, the elephant tusks, and the other wonderful things which they had gathered in the new land of Africa. When, sometimes, he sailed on a Portuguese caravel, he liked to hear the sailors tell stories about the adventures they had met in trying to sail to Asia, around Africa.

After a time, Columbus himself began to dream that he was

sailing to Asia, too, that great land which he was trying to paint on his brother's maps. He read the book which Marco Polo had written about his adventures in Asia, and other books which tried to show where China and India lay. He pored and pored over an old map which showed that the world was round.

"Since the world is round," Columbus said, "if one sails straight toward the setting sun from the west shore of Europe, one will reach Asia in a short time. It is silly for the Portuguese seamen to try to get to the Indies by going south round Africa and then east." (China, Japan, and India were all called the Indies at that time.) "It would be much simpler to sail west from Lisbon. I am going to tell the King of Portugal about all this; surely he will give me the ships."

The king, John of Portugal, was amazed at Columbus' idea.

"Hum! I never thought of that," he said. "How can you be sure that Asia lies so near, across that mysterious Atlantic Ocean which we can see from any window of my palaces?"

"I have studied old maps," answered Columbus. "I have also sailed to Iceland, the foggy isle of the north, where I heard sailors tell about a land to the west. The sea has also brought dead pine trees of a kind we have never seen in our countries. There is land not far across the Atlantic, I know. Truly if you give me some ships I'll find the countries Marco Polo told about—Japan, where the king's palace has roofs of gold; China, from whence comes our silk, and where there are so many rich and busy cities; India and the islands of the East from which come spices and precious stones.

"Of course, it is only fair that I have my reward for doing all this. I want to be made a knight with golden spurs; a great admiral of all the oceans; and governor of all the countries I will find. I also want the tenth part of all the riches I bring back to Lisbon."

"All that!" exclaimed the king. "Well, maybe your idea is

good, maybe it is not. I am not sure. I shall call the most learned scholars of Portugal to hear what they have to say."

The old scholars came, listened, looked scornful, and finally said, "No, no! This young man, Columbus, is just a dreamer. Only God knows how large the Atlantic Ocean is, and what lies beyond. Only a fool would try to sail across it, and he would not return."

Columbus went home broken-hearted.

"There are other kings who will like your idea," his brother Bartholomew told him. "Go and see the King of Spain, Ferdinand, and his Queen Isabella."

So Columbus took his dream into Spain and was heard by the Queen and King.

"I think there may be something in your idea," said the King.

"So do I," said the Queen. "But we are very busy now chasing the Moors out of Spain, and we have no time to study all that ourselves. Let's get together some learned scholars of Spain,

AMERICA

so they can hear what you have to say."

The Spanish scholars met, but could not make up their minds at once. Columbus waited and waited. Finally the scholars decided. They said no. But they added, "Wait until the Moors are out of Spain, then come back. Perhaps we will have changed our minds by then."

"No more waiting," said Columbus. "I am going to see the King of France."

And he departed for France.

But then, some of his friends went to Queen Isabella, and they talked so well about Columbus that she called him back.

"Perhaps you are right, after all," she said to him. "Perhaps you can bring us the spices and silks and precious stones of the East."

"I know I can."

"Then if I give you the ships, what will you ask in return?"

Columbus repeated what he had asked the King of Portugal.

"That's too much," exclaimed the queen, her eyes big with surprise.

COLUMBUS FINDS

"I would not do it for less," declared Columbus.

"Then we won't give the ships."

Columbus was quite angry now. He said good-by to his friends and again took the road to France.

However, the treasurer of the King and Queen, who was a wise man, said to Isabella,

"I think you should give Columbus what he wants. What can you lose? It does not cost much to give him the golden spurs and make him a knight. If he comes back from China with his ships full of treasures, wouldn't you rather give him one tenth and keep all the rest than have the King of France have it?"

"I would," said Queen Isabella. "Go after Columbus and catch him before he gets into France."

This second time, when Columbus came back to King Ferdinand and Queen Isabella, he was granted the ships and the rewards he asked.

It was in the Port of Palos in southern Spain that Columbus made his caravels ready. There were three of them: a large one, the *Santa Maria,* and two smaller ones, the *Pinta* and the *Niña.* On a misty summer dawn, in August, 1492, the three caravels spread their sails with the painted cross, and sailed away.

"Now," thought Columbus, standing on the high stern of the *Santa Maria,* "every minute that the wind blows, I am nearer Japan, China, and India. Soon I will be the great admiral of all the seas."

AMERICA

Columbus' sailors knew the Atlantic Ocean from Spain to the Canary Islands, which belonged to King Ferdinand. They were sure they would not meet horrible sea monsters until they arrived there. But beyond, it was another story. It was the very first time that ships had ventured straight onto an unknown sea with no land on either side.

"How can our captain be so sure that this ocean has an end?" wondered a young Spaniard. "For my part, I fear that we shall never return. Look, the wind blows steadily toward the West. We won't be able to get back with this wind always at our bow."

"In my time," said an old sailor, "I have heard many stories of ships swallowed by sea serpents; of ships falling off the earth at the end of the sea. I believe they are true stories."

While they frightened one another in this way with strange sea tales, the three caravels sailed on and on. The sailors thought of Spain, behind them. Columbus thought of Asia ahead of him.

One morning, they climbed the masts and rigging with joy after Captain Pinzon, master of the *Pinta,* had cried, "Land! Land!" But the next morning was like all the mornings before, nothing in sight but the blue waves which never tired of running after one another.

"If we go on, we are lost," growled the men. "Our place is in Spain with our wives and children, not on this awful sea with a captain who lives in a silly dream, full of Japans and Chinas."

"We shall not go on another day," they all said menacingly.

"Let's throw him overboard," an angry sailor cried. "Then we can turn round."

Columbus came out of his small cabin on the high aft castle, and looking at them without fear, said, "There is no use complaining. I have come to seek Japan, China, and India, and with the help of God, I will find them. Do not be afraid. You will go back to your families, with your hands full of gold."

COLUMBUS FINDS

Seeing that Columbus was so resolute, the seamen went back to their posts, though they still grumbled. They kept their eyes on the blue horizon, hoping for a sight of land.

As the days went by, there were many signs that land was not far off. Once, all night long, great flights of birds flew over the ships. One afternoon, a reed and carved stick floated by. At the end of that same day, as Columbus stood on the aft castle, watching the night ahead of him and listening to the waves as they broke on the sides of the *Santa Maria,* he saw a little light. "Look!" he cried to his sailors, "before us, at the bow. Do you see that light?"

"I see it," said one man.

"I don't!" said another.

"Perhaps it is another mistake, then," sighed Columbus.

But it was not, for soon after that, a sailor on the *Pinta* shouted,

"Land! Land! It's land, for sure."

Among cries of joy, Columbus ordered his ships to lie at anchor. Few sailors slept that night. Most of them stood on the decks, their eyes peering into the dark, like people in a theater waiting for the curtain to rise.

"What shall we see in the morning?" wondered Columbus. "The gold roofs of Japanese palaces, no doubt, for this land lies just where I thought Japan was —to the east of China. It must be Japan!"

At dawn, as darkness began to lift, a small island slowly took shape: a cool white beach; tall green palm trees, still wet with dew. All was quiet. Then a bird, hidden among the leaves, whistled, and others answered it. Some naked brown men came down to the water's edge, talking and yelling among themselves in a strange language, pointing to the big sailing vessels which the night had brought. Some of them had painted their bodies red; others had blue faces; a few had dipped their noses into yellow paint.

America lay before Columbus' eyes. It was October the twelfth, fourteen hundred and ninety-two.

"I don't understand!" murmured Columbus. "There are no gold roofs. In his book Marco Polo does not say that the Japanese and the Chinese go naked and painted. He does say that they wear rich robes of silk; and he also says that the seas around Japan are full of islands. That must be one of them."

Columbus now put on his most beautiful clothes and his coat of green velvet and landed on the shore, holding in his left hand the banner of the King of Spain. Behind him came the captains of the *Niña* and *Pinta,* carrying the flag with the green cross.

"From now on," Columbus declared, "this island will belong to King Ferdinand, and it will be called 'San Salvador' on the map." His scribes wrote that down, and Columbus and his officers scratched their names below it.

The painted brown men stood around them and wondered what it was all about. They would have been sad, had they known that the greedy white men would soon chase them out of their fairylike islands.

They smiled when the sailors gave them some glass beads, tinkling bells, and red bonnets. As they, too, wanted to be generous, they brought presents of cotton balls, green parrots, fruits, and arrows.

"There is nothing much in this small island," Columbus said. "I am impatient to go and look for Japan and China. All aboard!"

There were many islands in these seas, all very green and beautiful. They were full of new kinds of flowers and fruits, with birds of all colors flying among the palm trees. But nowhere did Columbus find the rich cities, busy with hundreds of laden ships, which Marco Polo had seen in China. Nowhere did the gold roofs of the palaces of the King of Japan glitter above the trees. There were but the straw huts of the naked men. Since Columbus thought he had come to the Indies, he called them Indians. And Indians they are still called.

"Where are those rich palaces, those people clothed in silk?" asked Columbus. "It is time to sail back to Spain and I have not found them. I shall have to come back and look some more."

When the *Pinta* and the *Niña* made their way back across the Atlantic Ocean, they did not carry embroidered robes of silk and satin like the ones Marco Polo brought back to Venice. In their place were Indians, a few noisy green parrots, balls of cotton, fruits, arrows, and some bits of gold jewelry.

After landing in Palos, Columbus went to see King Ferdinand and Queen Isabella in the city of Barcelona. He entered it to the sound of trumpets and drums, amidst flying banners.

The king and queen were pleased with his discoveries. His fame spread over Europe. He was now a knight, Don Cristóbal Columbus, great admiral of all the oceans, with golden spurs.

Columbus made three more voyages across the ocean to the West. He found more islands, and he also saw the shores of South America and of Central America. He died soon after his fourth voyage, without knowing that he had added to the map one of the biggest and richest continents of the world.

Adapted from *They Went to Sea*

Pocahontas and Captain John Smith

By Ingri and Edgar Parin D'Aulaire

IN THE year 1607 the first Englishmen came sailing across the ocean to settle the part of the new world which they called Virginia after their virgin queen, Elizabeth. They might all have perished if it had not been for the help they got from the Indian Princess Pocahontas. This is her story.

In the dark woods of Virginia, where dusky owls hooted over the treetops and prowling beasts howled at the moon, there lived a stern old Indian chief. His name was Powhatan, and he ruled over thirty tribes.

He had a little daughter who was the very apple of his eye. She was as sweet and pretty as he was ugly and cruel.

He gave her the finest feathers and the shiniest shells when he came home from the warpath, for he was so very fond of her.

"Oh, that little one is sweet, but full of pranks, and only wants to play," said the squaws. They worked from morning till night and their girls had to help them. But the mighty Powhatan's dearest daughter was allowed to skip and dance.

He gave her the name *Pocahontas,* which means *the one who plays mostly.* She ran and frolicked in woods and fair meadows. She grew strong and straight and supple as a cat, and could find her way in the deepest forest.

Then one day white men came to Powhatan's land. Their like the Indians had never seen. On huge boats they were blown straight in from the great waters. From their boats roared the voice of thunder itself. At once they began to build a village in Powhatan's land. They chopped down his trees. They hunted his game, and acted as though they owned his land. They were not afraid of offending Powhatan, even though he was so mighty that everyone trembled when he frowned.

They must be dangerous sorcerers, Powhatan's people thought. It wasn't only that they did not look like regular people, with their pale faces and their hair like corn silk. But in their hands they carried magic sticks that spat fire which killed whatever it hit.

Yes, they were so dangerous and full of sorcery that even Powhatan did not go against them quickly with all his braves to chase them out of his land. His medicine man sat at his side and juggled and conjured to try to find out what kind of magic the pale-faces practiced, but he could not make it out.

All that summer the Indians worried and wondered, and the children cried and went into hiding when anybody said,"Paleface."

One day Pocahontas sat in the garden, playing with a doll she had made of a corncob. Suddenly she laughed right out loud! The palefaces looked just like her corncob doll.

Then she was certain their magic could not be evil, for corn was the Indian's best friend.

When fall came the Indians captured one of the white leaders. He had ventured too far away from the white men's village and a band of Indian warriors caught him in a swamp. They dragged

him through the woods to Powhatan's village, so the mighty chief himself could decide what should be done with him.

Powhatan called his medicine man and the medicine man called his helpers. They painted their faces in the most awesome manner with green and red and black paint, and the medicine man adorned his head with stuffed snakes and weasels.

When the prisoner was brought into the village the children yelled. But Pocahontas was not the least bit afraid. She thought he was the handsomest man she had ever seen. His eyes were strange and blue as the sky, but she could see no evil in them.

She painted her face a glowing red and hurried into her ceremonial robe of white turkey feathers, so she could take her place beside her father when he judged the prisoner.

He was an English captain and his name was John Smith. He was the hardiest and shrewdest of the white men who had come to Powhatan's land.

In Powhatan's longhouse John Smith faced the chief bravely. With words and with signs he answered all questions outright. Powhatan looked pleased with what he heard. "My father will let him live," thought Pocahontas. But the medicine men were scowling as they danced and shouted and worked their magic.

At last they spoke to Powhatan, and said that the spirits had told them the white man's magic was evil, the prisoner must die. But as the medicine men made ready to kill John Smith, Pocahontas suddenly rushed forward. She took his head in her arms and laid her head upon his to save him from death.

The medicine men grumbled, but Powhatan said the prisoner should live. For there was a custom among the Indians that a maiden could save a prisoner from death if she had taken a liking to him. Then he was her property.

So the English captain and the little Indian princess became fast friends. He whittled dolls and toys for her with his sharp knife of steel and showed her some of his things, which the Indians thought were magic.

In his big pocket he had many strange things. There was a little spirit that lived in a box. This spirit always pointed straight to the north. With it John Smith could never get lost in the thickest woods. It really was a compass, but to Pocahontas it was magic.

He told about his country, England, far away on the other side of the sea, and about his chief, who was the King of England. This King was still mightier than Powhatan. His house of snow-white stone was as large as a whole Indian village. There, little princesses ran about clad in silk and silver and gold and played with pearls and diamonds.

Of more and more wondrous things he talked, until even Powhatan was so impressed that he called John Smith his son and said if he wanted he might return to Jamestown, the white men's village.

So John Smith bade good-by to his little Indian princess and said, "My priceless jewel, bring me your little basket and I will fill it with blue beads."

The other Indian girls all envied Pocahontas her beautiful beads. But to her nothing seemed much fun after her white friend had left. When she heard that John Smith and his people were sick and hungry in their village, she begged and prayed till her father let her go to them with food. She filled great baskets with corn and asked her playmates to help her carry them. Leading the procession through the woods, she trudged the long way to Jamestown. Many times that winter Pocahontas came with food for the settlers.

A few years passed and Pocahontas grew to be a beautiful maiden. John Smith returned to England, but among her friends in Jamestown there was a young man whose name was John Rolfe. He grew so fond of her that he felt he could not live without her. He said he would give her all that he had in the world and always be kind to her if she would marry him. Yes, maybe some day he would even take her to England.

She gave him her hand and vowed to marry him if her father said yes. That he did.

So Pocahontas was christened and named Rebecca, for she must also have a Christian name. Then they had the wedding in Jamestown and made merry and feasted for many days.

When some time had passed, Pocahontas had a little boy child. He was pinker than a white child and paler than an Indian child.

POCAHONTAS AND CAPTAIN JOHN SMITH

The Indians said, "Oh, he will be darker when he grows up." The white people said, "Oh, he will be fairer when he grows up." But to Pocahontas he was the most beautiful child in the whole world.

It was told about in England that one of the Jamestown settlers had married an Indian princess. Everyone who heard about her wanted to see what she looked like. Soon it was decided that John Rolfe should take his family to England for a visit.

Oh, how happy Pocahontas was. Now she would see for herself the wondrous things that John Smith had told her about. They sailed for days and they sailed for weeks and they sailed for months. At last they came to an English port.

Much ado was made of Pocahontas. Great ladies opened their doors to her. They gave balls and banquets in her honor and took her to the theater to see plays written by William Shakespeare. Artists painted her portrait. Poets wrote songs in her honor. Her name was on everyone's lips.

Then one day, whom should Pocahontas see but John Smith! There he stood among all the strangers. He bowed low before Pocahontas and called her Lady Rebecca. He had not forgotten his little Indian friend.

Pocahontas never returned to her home across the great water. But when her son was a grown man, he sailed to his mother's country. There he became the father of a great big family.

Adapted from *Pocahontas*

The True Story of
Benjamin Franklin

By Elbridge S. Brooks

ONE DAY when Benjamin Franklin was about seven years old there was a holiday in Boston. As a holiday present Benjamin was given a handful of pennies, and started out for a good time, feeling as rich as a lord. He made a straight line for the toy shop; but, on his way, he met a boy blowing a whistle. It was shrill and clear, and at once Ben decided that he wished for a whistle more than anything else. So he asked the boy to sell it, and offered his handful of pennies in exchange. The other boy took all he could get, of course, and Ben walked away, feeling very proud of his purchase.

Soon he was in the house, whistling with all his might. But the Franklin family laughed, when they found what Ben had paid for the whistle. "A fine tradesman you are," they said. "Why, you might have bought four whistles at the toy shop for what you have paid for one. Think what you might have bought with your money—and a whistle besides."

Ben always remembered the lesson he had learned that day. More than sixty years afterwards, when he wrote the story of his life, he said, "I cried with vexation; and my reflections gave me more chagrin than the whistle gave me pleasure. When I was tempted to buy some unnecessary thing, I said to myself, 'Don't pay too much for the whistle!' and so saved my money."

But he was a wise little fellow, even if he did sometimes get sold; and his playmates knew it. They found him to be a good comrade, jolly, venturesome, full of plans, just the boy to be a leader in sports and, sometimes, in pranks.

One of these pranks got him into trouble. Down near what is now Boston's crowded water front, there used to be a marsh. It was a fine place to catch minnows at high tide, and Ben and the other boys did a great deal of fishing there. They went there so much that they often trampled the low bank into a mudhole.

"That ought to be fixed," said Ben. "Let's build a wharf." The boys found a pile of stones near by and lugged them to the minnow marsh. Working like beavers, they soon had a fishing wharf. But the stones had been intended for the cellar of a new house, and when the workmen who were building it discovered what had happened, there was a great fuss. Ben was found to have been at the bottom of the scheme and was quickly taken to task.

He took his punishment like a man; but he argued with his father that he ought not to be punished. The stones were there; the boys just *had* to have a wharf; they had built a good one. But his father did not agree. "The stones were not yours to take, Ben," he said. "What is not honest cannot be truly useful."

So Ben Franklin learned another lesson, which stayed by him all through his eventful life; that "honesty is the best policy."

This marsh was one of Ben's favorite playgrounds. During his boyhood, Boston was half water, and Ben always loved the water. He was a good hand in a boat; he was a strong and fearless swimmer.

One of his earliest inventions was connected with swimming. He wished to fix up something so that he could swim long and far, and he tried two experiments. Once he got up a sort of push-board or pallet for his hands, and also a broad kind of sandal or swimming shoe for his feet. These worked fairly well; but the best help he found was to fly a kite. Fastening the string to his wrist, he let the kite pull him through the water, while he lay quietly on his back, lowering or raising the kite as he wished to go faster or slower.

Ben was a bright boy, and he once said he did not remember when he could not read. He started to school early, and, at eight years of age, was in the grammar school. He stood at the head of his class, and was promoted to higher classes twice within a year. Then he was sent to a "writing-school" to learn writing and arithmetic. But life was a hard struggle in the big Franklin family. When Ben was ten, his father, a candlemaker, took him out of school and put him to work in his own shop.

His son, however, did not want to be a candlemaker. He hated to cut wicks and make moulds and run grease; he hated the touch and the smell. "I don't like it," he said. "I'd rather go to sea."

Now, one of the Franklin boys had run away to sea, and the father did not wish to lose another in that way. When he saw that

THE TRUE STORY OF BENJAMIN FRANKLIN

Ben really did dislike the trade of a candlemaker, he decided to make him a printer. So Ben became an apprentice in the printing shop of his elder brother, James.

At the same time he set out to educate himself. He soon struck up an acquaintance with a number of boys who worked for the Boston booksellers. They would loan him books from their shelves, and he would sit up late at night—sometimes almost all night—to read the book through and have it back at the bookstore next morning. What little money he had to spend—and it was very little—he put into books. He read everything he could get hold of. Up early in the morning, up late at night, he put every spare moment to use.

Ben's brother called his newspaper the *New England Courant.* There were very few newspapers in the world then—only four in all America, and three of these in Boston. Ben was a very busy boy—setting type for the *Courant,* printing it, folding it, and delivering it to the subscribers. He was office boy, compositor, printer, and newsboy all in one. But James Franklin was a hard man to get along with, and Ben's lot was not a happy one. He was an independent youth and used to speaking his mind. He fretted under his brother's tyranny, and often "talked back." Sometimes there were blows from the elder brother, until at last Ben felt he could not stand it any longer.

Finally he told James that he would not work for him any more, but James said he would have to.

"I will not," said Ben. "There are other printers in Boston."

"I'll fix them," said James.

And he did. He went to every printer in town, and told them that his brother Ben was bound to him until he was twenty-one, and that they would get into trouble if they employed him. So, when the boy went about town looking for a new job, he could not get one.

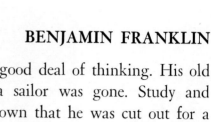

BENJAMIN FRANKLIN

Ben did a good deal of thinking. His old desire to be a sailor was gone. Study and success had shown that he was cut out for a printer, and a printer he would be. There were but three towns in all America large enough to support printers: Boston, New York, and Philadelphia. In Boston he could not and would not remain. So he decided to run away and go to New York. He sold some of his precious books to pay his passage, and a friend smuggled him on board a sailing vessel.

Thus it happened that on a certain October morning in the year 1723, Ben Franklin, aged seventeen, a runaway apprentice, bade a silent good-by to his boyhood home, and was soon on blue water, bound for new adventures.

Unable to find a job in New York, Ben went on to Philadelphia. When he arrived he had left only one silver dollar and about twenty cents in coppers. He stepped out on the wharf, dirty, bedraggled, hungry, sleepy, and seedy—a tramp printer looking for a job.

But Ben was not a boy who was easily discouraged. He soon found a job as a printer, and later became Philadelphia's most honored citizen. During the next sixty years, he gave most of his time to winning freedom and glory for his native land. And no man ever did so many things for the comfort and benefit of mankind.

He improved the printing press. He invented stoves. He made double spectacles for near and farsighted people. He taught men that lightning was electricity, and invented lightning rods. He founded the first public library, the first fire company, the first police service, the first magazine.

Adapted from *The True Story of Benjamin Franklin*

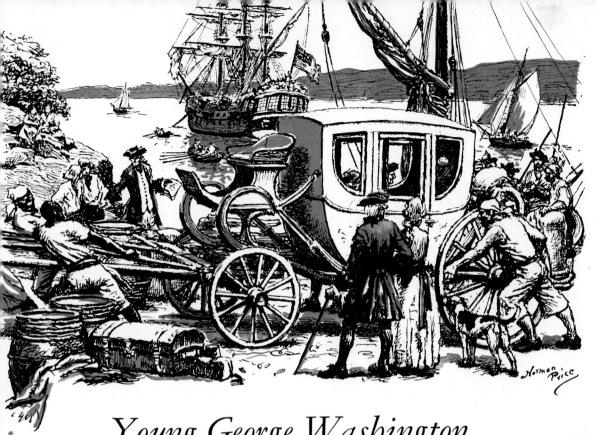

Young George Washington

By James Baldwin

WHEN George Washington was a boy in Virginia, once every summer a ship came up the river to the plantation.

It had come across the sea from far-away England, and it brought many things for those who were rich enough to pay for them. It brought bonnets and pretty dresses for George's mother and sisters. It brought perhaps a hat and a tailor-made suit for himself. It brought tools and furniture and, once, a yellow coach that had been made in London for his brother.

When all these things had been taken ashore, the ship would hoist her sails and go on farther up the river, to leave goods at other plantations.

In a few weeks it would come back and be moored again at the same place. Then there was a busy time on shore. The tobacco that had been raised during the last year must be carried on shipboard to be taken to the great tobacco markets in England. The slaves on the plantation were running back and forth, rolling barrels and carrying bales of tobacco down to the landing. Letters were written to friends in England, and orders were made out for the goods that were to be brought back next year.

But in a day or two, all this stir was over. The sails were again spread, and the ship glided away on its long voyage across the sea.

George had seen this ship coming and going every year since he could remember. He must have thought how pleasant it would be to sail away to foreign lands and see the many wonderful things that are there. And then, like many another active boy, he began to grow tired of the quiet life on the farm, and wish that he might be a sailor.

He was now about fourteen years old, and his father had been dead for three years. His mother, with her five children, found it hard work to manage her farm on the Rappahannock River and make everything come out even at the end of each year. Was it not time that George should be earning something for himself? But what should he do?

He wanted to go to sea. His elder half-brother, Lawrence, and even his mother thought that this might be the best thing. A bright boy like George would not long be a common sailor. He would soon make his way to a high place in the King's navy. So, at least, his friends believed.

The matter was at last settled. A sea captain, who was known to the family, agreed to take George with him. He was to sail in a short time. But in the meantime a letter had come to his mother, from his uncle who lived in England.

"If you care for the boy's future," said the letter, "do not let him go to sea. Places in the King's navy are not easy to obtain. If he begins as a sailor, he will never be aught else."

The letter convinced George's mother—it half-convinced his brothers—that this going to sea would be a sad mistake. But

YOUNG GEORGE WASHINGTON

George, like other boys of his age, was headstrong. He would not listen to reason. A sailor he would be.

The ship was in the river waiting for him. A boat had come to the landing to take him on board. The little chest which held his clothing had been carried down to the bank. George was in high glee at the thought of going.

"Good-by, Mother," he said.

He stood on the doorstep and looked back into the house. He saw the kind faces of those whom he loved. He began to feel very sad at the thought of leaving them.

"Good-by, George!"

He saw the tears welling up in his mother's eyes. He knew now that she did not want him to go. He could not bear to see her grief.

"Mother, I have changed my mind," he said. "I will not be a sailor. I will not leave you."

Then he turned to the colored boy who was waiting by the door, and said, "Run down to the landing and tell them not to put the chest on board. Tell them that I have thought differently of the matter and that I am going to stay at home."

After George Washington had changed his mind about going to sea, he studied surveying. His brother, Lawrence, had married and built a large house at Mount Vernon, with a great porch fronting on the Potomac River. Here George went to live, for Lawrence had great love for the boy, and treated him as his father would have done.

At Mount Vernon George kept on with his studies in surveying. He had a compass and surveyor's chain, and hardly a day passed that he was not out on the plantation, measuring his brother's fields.

Sometimes while he was working, a tall, white-haired gentleman would come over from Belvoir, the neighboring plantation, to talk with him. This gentleman was Sir Thomas Fairfax, who had

lately come from England to look after his lands in Virginia. For he was the owner of many thousands of acres among the mountains and in the wild woods. He hoped that when the land had been surveyed, and some part of it laid out in farms, people might be persuaded to go there and settle.

It was not long before Sir Thomas and George were the best of friends. Often they would spend the morning together, talking or surveying; and in the afternoon they would ride out with hounds, hunting foxes and making fine sport of it among the woods and hills. Sir Thomas Fairfax saw how brave his young friend was, and how exact and careful in all that he did.

"Here is a boy who gives promise of great things," he said to himself. "I can trust him."

Before the winter was over, he had made a bargain with his

YOUNG GEORGE WASHINGTON

young friend to survey his lands that lay beyond the Blue Ridge Mountains. George had many exciting adventures on that trip, and Sir Thomas was well pleased with his work. Through his influence George Washington was appointed public surveyor.

His experience as a surveyor in the wilderness led George into other great adventures. When he was twenty-three, he was chosen to carry an important message to the French soldiers who were trying to get control of the Ohio River Valley. The French and Indian War came after that, and George served as a soldier. Later he became a great general in the War for Independence and helped the English colonies to become a new nation—the United States of America. He was the first President of the United States, and was so well loved that it was said of him: "He was first in war, first in peace, and first in the hearts of his countrymen."

Adapted from *Four Great Americans*

Alexander Mackenzie, A Hero of Canada

By Maxine Shore and M. M. Oblinger

ONCE again Alexander Mackenzie was going on a trip—this time to Montreal. Astride a small roan mare, Alex was remembering another journey which had changed his life, as this one would surely do. At ten, he had left his birthplace in the Hebrides, off the coast of Scotland, to sail across the Atlantic to the thriving New World settlement of New York. A year later rebellion had broken out in the American colonies, but the Mackenzies were Loyalists; that is, they had remained loyal to the British King. There were many bitter quarrels and sometimes fighting between those who were loyal to the King and those who were not, and many Loyalists were forced to flee to Canada.

His aunts had insisted that Alex join a party of Loyalist refugees, and had promised to join him later in Montreal. As the refugee train plunged into deeper and deeper wilderness, he had a chance

to become well acquainted with his aunt's friend, Mrs. McDonell, a brisk woman past middle age.

"It is a terrible thing when God-fearing, law-abiding settlers are forced from their hard-earned homes," she told Alex grimly. "This new country should be big enough, land knows, for everybody."

"How big?" asked Alex.

"America? Well, no one knows exactly. No one's been clear across it to find out yet."

"They haven't!" Alex, amazed, turned his head to look westward. How could folks be content not to know? Didn't anyone care what lay beyond?

Mrs. McDonell gave him an understanding glance, "All young lads hunger for the horizon, Alex. But most grow out of it."

35

ALEXANDER MACKENZIE, A HERO OF CANADA

Young Alexander Mackenzie drew a deep, steady breath. "I won't," he said.

Montreal! Was there ever a fairer town? After a few months Alex began to feel that he had always lived there. Mrs. McDonell treated him like a son, and her many relatives welcomed him kindly. Alex explored his romantic new surroundings eagerly, whenever he could. Beyond the town lay the gardens, orchards, and beautiful estates of the aristocracy. There, too, were the charming farms of the *habitants,* the humbler French settlers who worked the land.

And when he tired of tramping the quiet, fragrant earth, there was always the water front to visit. The ceaseless coming and going had for him a breathless appeal. Having learned French easily, he would listen to the stories and *chansons* (*songs*) of the French *voyageurs* (*travelers*) who carried on a fur trade with the Indians. High in the returning *bateaux* (*boats*) were piled the shining peltries, and Alex began to realize that furs were the wealth of the North. At Montreal the furs were stored and packed for shipment to England, there to be sold. But this rich commerce depended upon the friendliness of the Indians, who could be won with strings of bright beads, looking glasses, warm English-woven blankets, and tobacco.

The first spring after Alex arrived in Montreal, he haunted the water front. He was fascinated by watching the skillful canoemen load the canoes with trade goods, supplies, and ammunition for the trip into the interior. So absorbed was he one morning that he was not aware when someone came up behind him. Stepping back out of the way of a busy worker, he trampled the toes of Simon McTavish, one of the wealthiest and most important of the fur traders.

Mr. McTavish brought his cane down hard on the boy's shoulders. "Learn some manners, young scoundrel!"

Alex's eyes smarted from the stinging blow. "I'm no scoundrel, sir. If I stepped on you, I'm sorry. But it was an accident. Surely—"

ALEXANDER MACKENZIE, A HERO OF CANADA

"Surely—" Again the cane rapped him smartly—"surely I'll not be talked back to."

Flaming with indignation, Alex threw back his dark curly head. Mr. McTavish's lips were set in a thin, tight line. He was a tall haughty man—without doubt a man to be feared and obeyed by the voyageurs and others who had to do business with him. But Alex was not inclined to do either.

"Surely," he said, "I will not be caned after proper apology." His brilliant wide-set eyes met those of the older man defiantly.

Simon McTavish's brows drew together over his nose in a black frown. "Will you not, young rascal? Indeed, 'tis time you were taught respect for your betters."

Simon McTavish, paling with anger, raised his stick again purposefully. But before it could descend, Alex caught it and wrenched it away. He flung it to the ground.

With an outraged roar, McTavish reached for him. Alex turned and ran, ducking through the crowd of Indians and voyageurs. He plunged into a dim street. Behind him he could hear running feet.

A habitant's cart blocked his way. Desperately, he darted into the dark doorway of a shop. He would hide here until his pursuer went by.

But the man who had followed had seen where Alex went. He hurried toward him. "Young man, are you Alexander Mackenzie?"

"Y-yes, sir." No use to flee now. They knew his name. They could track him down wherever he was, and mete out fitting punishment to a boy who had been impudent to the great Simon McTavish.

"I'm John Gregory, lad."

The man was smiling—actually he was holding out his hand!

"Good day to you, sir," faltered Alex.

The name of John Gregory he recognized instantly, a noted one in the fur business. He was a partner of the firm of Gregory and

McLeod. Alex had often passed the business house with that inscription on the door.

Mr. Gregory was considering him earnestly. Alex shifted uneasily. Finally, John Gregory nodded, as if satisfied.

"Young man," he said, "you are the first, boy or man, who ever stood up to Simon McTavish."

"Oh, sir, it was all an accident. I never meant—"

"You mean you're sorry?"

"Oh, yes, sir. That is, I'm sorry it happened."

"And you'll never do it again?"

Alex took a long, uneven breath. "I cannot promise," he said. "After I've made proper apology for a mistake, I don't mean to be caned by anyone."

The Englishman's eyes, oddly enough, were twinkling. He reached a hand to Alex's shoulder.

"Lad, I could use a clerk like you in my business."

Alex could not speak. It was as if Mr. Gregory had dug into his very mind and brought forth his greatest desire. He was fifteen now, wanting to earn his own livelihood and to take care of his aunts, too, if necessary. If his aunts were anything like the other Loyalists pouring into Canada, they would probably be almost destitute when they arrived. It was high time, Alex resolved, to prove himself a man.

"Oh, sir," he cried eagerly, "I'd like nothing better than to go into the fur business. I'll work hard, I promise. You'll never be sorry for giving me this chance."

John Gregory smiled. "I'm sure of that, lad. You're a likely young man. 'Tis my opinion you'll go far."

Promising to report early the following morning, Alex parted from Mr. Gregory. He walked down the street, his thoughts dancing with excitement. The day's misfortune had been transformed miraculously into fortune. Opportunity had knocked, and his future stretched ahead invitingly.

When Alex grew up, he became a famous fur trader and explorer. He discovered the Mackenzie River, which was named for him. Three years later he blazed a new trail all the way to the Pacific Ocean. He was the first white man who ever reached the Pacific Ocean by crossing the northern part of the continent, but his journey was more than mere high-hearted adventure. He discovered a fabulously rich country, and opened a new land for people to live in. His journey made history, for it did more than any one thing to weld the territories of the North together in one country—Canada, a great commonwealth of free men.

Adapted from *Knight of the Wilderness*

The Boy Lafayette and the Wolf

By James Baldwin

IN FRANCE there once lived a famous man who was known as the Marquis de Lafayette. When he was a little boy his mother called him Gilbert.

Gilbert de Lafayette's father and grandfather and great-grandfather had all been brave and noble men. He wished that he might grow up to be like them.

His home was in the country not far from a great forest. Often, when he was a little boy, he took long walks among the trees with his mother. "Mother," he would say, "do not be afraid. I am with you, and I will not let anything hurt you."

One day word came that a savage wolf had been seen in the forest. Men said that it was a very large wolf and that it had killed some of the farmers' sheep.

"How I should like to meet that wolf," said Gilbert.

He was only seven years old, but now all his thoughts were about the savage beast that was

40

in the forest.

"Shall we take a walk this morning?" asked his mother.

"Oh, yes!" said Gilbert. "Perhaps we may see that wolf among the trees. But don't be afraid."

His mother smiled, for she felt quite sure that there was no danger.

They did not go far into the woods. The mother sat down in the shade of a tree and began to read a new book which she had bought the day before. The boy played on the grass near by.

The sun was warm. The bees were buzzing among the flowers. The birds were singing softly. Gilbert looked up from his play and saw that his mother was deeply interested in her book.

"Now for the wolf!" he said to himself.

He walked quickly, but quietly, down the pathway into the darker woods. He looked eagerly around, but saw only a squirrel frisking among the trees and a rabbit hopping across the road.

Soon he came to a wilder place. There the bushes were very close together and the pathway came to an end. He pushed the bushes aside and went a little farther. How still everything was!

He could see a green open space just beyond; and then the woods seemed to be thicker and darker.

"This is just the place for that wolf," he thought.

Then, all at once, he heard footsteps. Something was pushing its way through the bushes. It was coming toward him.

"It's the wolf, I'm sure! It will not see me till it comes very near. Then I will jump out and throw my arms around its neck and choke it to death."

The animal was coming nearer. He could hear its footsteps. He

could hear its heavy breathing. He stood very still and waited.

"It will try to bite me," he thought. "Perhaps it will scratch me with its sharp claws. But I will be brave. I will not cry out. I will choke it with my strong arms. Then I will drag it out of the bushes and call mamma to come and see it."

The beast was very close to him now. He could see its shadow as he peeped out through the clusters of leaves. His breath came fast. He planted his feet firmly and made ready to spring.

Ah, there was the wolf! He saw its shaggy head and big round eyes. He leaped from his hiding place and clasped it round its neck.

It did not try to bite or scratch. It did not even growl. But it jumped quickly forward and threw Gilbert upon the ground. Then it ran out into the open space and stopped to gaze at him.

Gilbert was soon on his feet again. He was not hurt at all. He looked at the beast, and—what do you think it was?

THE BOY LAFAYETTE AND THE WOLF

It was not a wolf. It was only a pet calf that had come there to browse among the bushes.

The boy felt very much ashamed. He hurried back to the pathway, and then ran to his mother. Tears were in his eyes but he tried to look brave.

"Oh, Gilbert, where have you been?" said his mother.

Then he told her. His lips quivered and he began to cry.

"Never mind, my dear," said his mother. "You were very brave, and it is lucky that the wolf was not there. You faced what you thought was a great danger, and you were not afraid. You are my hero."

Marquis de Lafayette became a soldier when he grew up and helped the American people during the American Revolution. He was the friend of General Washington. He is remembered as a hero who helped the United States to become free and independent.

From *Fifty Famous People*

Daniel Boone's New Home in Kentucky

By Enid LaMonte Meadowcroft

"WHY doesn't Pa come home, Jamie?" asked Jemima Boone, looking at her brothers. "I'm so worried about him. Do you think the Indians have killed him?"

"Maybe," James said, soberly. "Or maybe he's lost in the wilderness. Or maybe—"

Israel broke in quickly. "Don't you talk that way, James Boone!" he exclaimed. "Our Pa can take care of himself anywhere. When he went away he said he was going to find that place the Indians call Kentucky. He'll find it, too. And one of these days he'll come back from there with his horses loaded down with meat and furs. He will, James, I know he will."

A few days later Israel was sitting on the log step before the cabin in North Carolina where the Boone family lived. He had hoed the corn, which was now two inches high. He had hauled

44

in logs from the woodpile for his mother's fire. He had helped James bring the cows in from the forest and milk them. Now he just wanted to sit still until his mother called him in to supper.

Often he sat listening like this, for some day he meant to be a great hunter like his father, Daniel Boone. And he knew that great hunters must have well-trained ears.

They must be able to hear the least little rustling of trees and bushes. They must catch the sound of a snapping twig. They must know the bird calls, and the noise that the wild turkey makes, and all the other big and little sounds of the deep forest.

The sounds that came loudest to Israel's ears now were the sounds from the cabin behind him. Through the open door he could hear the whirring of his mother's spinning wheel.

He could hear the voices of his sisters, Jemima and Susannah, who were getting supper. And he could hear the laughter of the little children, Lavinia and Danny, who were playing on the cabin floor.

Beyond the clearing the sweet call of a wood thrush came to his ears. A squirrel chattered noisily. Far away a crow cawed. And a neighbor's hound dog barked twice.

Then, from far down the winding road, there came a sound that brought Israel to his feet in an instant.

"Hello, Boones!" a man's voice called in the distance. "Hello there, Boones!"

"Pa has come," Israel shouted joyfully. "Pa has come, everybody! Pa is home!"

And he raced off down the road as though he had been shot from a cannon.

Inside the cabin Susannah, his sister, cried, "Pa's come home!" She put down the noggin of milk she was carrying and snatched Danny from the floor.

Jemima grabbed Lavinia by the hand. Mrs. Boone jumped up

from her spinning wheel. James dropped the moccasin he was mending. Together they all crowded through the cabin door. And they ran down the road as fast as they could go.

It was just light enough for them to see Daniel Boone. He was coming round the bend of the road. He was all alone, and he was walking.

Israel reached him first. "I knew you would come! I knew you would come!" he cried joyfully. And he threw his arms around his father.

Mr. Boone hugged him close. He shook James by the hand. Then he held out his arms to his wife and the girls. Mrs. Boone cried a little with happiness and everyone asked questions at once as they ran to hug him.

"Are you all right?"

"Why did you stay so long?"

"Did you find Kentucky?"

"What have you done with the pack horses?"

"Where have you been all this time?"

"Did you have any trouble with Indians?"

Mr. Boone laughed. "Hold on a minute," he said. "I am hungry enough to eat six porcupines, quills and all. Give me time to get a good meal under my belt. Then I will tell you everything."

When they sat down to supper, Israel was too excited to eat. He could not wait any longer to begin asking questions.

"Where are your horses, Pa, and your meat and skins?" he asked.

"The Indians stole them," Mr. Boone announced. "They caught me, too. They caught me twice. But I fooled them. Each time I got away."

"Did you find that Kentucky country?" asked Israel, as his father reached for the loaf of bread at the other end of the table.

"Yes, I found Kentucky," he said, cutting off a big slice of bread with his hunting knife. "I reckon I saw every little bit of it, too." Then he looked at his wife. "Kentucky is a fine land, Ma," he told her between bites. "There aren't any white men around to scare off the game. So the deer come right out on the meadows— thousands of them, all as fat as our hogs at killing time.

"Wild ducks and geese and turkeys fly all around. And the buffalo! Why, there are so many buffalo that the noise of their hoofs is louder than the loudest thunder you ever heard."

He stopped and looked around at his family. "How would you all like to go out and live in Kentucky?" he asked. "I found a mighty pretty spot out there where we can build us a nice cabin."

For a moment everyone at the table was too surprised to speak. Then Jemima exclaimed, "Oh, Pa, I'd like it!"

"So would I," agreed James.

"Me, too," Israel said. And he grinned from ear to ear.

But Mrs. Boone looked down at little Danny, who had fallen asleep in her arms, and shook her head.

"No, Dan," she said. "We don't want to move to Kentucky. A cabin out in the Indians' country is no place for children to grow up."

"It isn't the Indians' country," Daniel Boone declared. "There are no Indians living there. They hunt there and they fight there. But to my mind the country doesn't belong to any of them because they don't live there."

"I don't want to go," Susannah declared. "It will be lonesome out there with nothing but Indians and wild animals. I want—"

Her father interrupted her. "Maybe it won't be so lonesome," he said. "Maybe we can get some of our neighbors to go along, too. We'll build us a fort and make our own settlement. Why, some day maybe we'll even have a school there and a Sunday meeting- house."

He looked at his wife again. "How about it, Ma?" he asked.

"Will you come out there with me?"

Mrs. Boone did not answer for a minute. At last she said slowly, "Yes, if you want to try to start a settlement in Kentucky, and if you can get some other families to go along, we'll go with you."

Through the years that followed, thousands of families traveled over the road Boone had blazed, to settle in the West and to help build America.

From *On Indian Trails with Daniel Boone*

The Story of Dolly Madison

By Helen A. Monsell

HER NAME wasn't Dolly Madison when she was born. It was Dolly Payne. When she was a little Quaker girl living in Virginia, not many people had ever heard of her. The Revolutionary War was going on and nobody had time to pay much attention to children.

But when she grew up, she married James Madison, who became the fourth President of the United States. So then she was called Dolly Madison, and as Dolly Madison she is remembered ever since.

There was now a brand-new city on the banks of the Potomac River, named for George Washington. It was built expressly to be the capital of these new United States. There was a very new house in this very new city. It was built for the President of the United States.

The big White House was Dolly's own home for eight years. And how she enjoyed it! She gave fine dinners for her husband's friends. She had teas and receptions and parties of every kind.

Now, at last, she could wear the beautiful clothes she had

always longed for when she was a little girl. They were finer even than anything she had ever dreamed about. As a little Quaker girl, Dolly could never have imagined herself in a dress of rose-colored satin, with a white velvet train two yards long! She never even dreamed of a gold girdle with a gold necklace and bracelets, or of ostrich tips in her hair, with a gold-embroidered crown. Yet she wore all these one night at the President's reception.

But it wasn't because of her fine clothes that everybody knew Dolly and loved her. It wasn't because of her dinners and parties. It was because she liked to help other people enjoy themselves. She liked to make them comfortable.

And when she made a promise, she kept it.

During the War of 1812 the enemy was very near Washington. Many people were leaving the city. But Dolly was not afraid.

"I shall wait until my husband comes back," she said.

There was a very valuable painting of George Washington by Gilbert Stuart which hung in her dining room.

"Do you suppose it is safe?" asked Mrs. Washington's grandson. "If the enemy should break through—"

"Don't worry," said Dolly. "I'll see that it is taken care of."

But the next day there was fighting only a few miles from the city. It was so close that Dolly could hear the cannon. Then the American troops began to give way.

Soon the streets of Washington were filled with people rushing to get across the river before the enemy arrived.

"The Redcoats are coming! They will burn the town!"

At last two messengers came dashing up to the White House. They were covered with dust. They brought Dolly word from her husband: "We have lost. You must leave at once."

The day before, Dolly had packed her husband's most valuable Government papers into trunks that would fill her carriage. There was no room for her own belongings. Now, as she hurried through

the dining room, she could pick up only what little silver she could crowd into her handbag.

But there was George Washington's picture. She couldn't leave that. She had promised it would be taken care of.

It was a large painting. Its back was screwed to the wall. It was hung so high one had to climb on a stepladder to reach it.

"Hurry! Hurry!" cried Dolly's friends. "You must leave at once."

But Dolly called to her servant. "Come, John, we must get the picture down, first."

There was no time to take it from its frame.

"Get your ax and break the frame," said Dolly.

And, no matter how great the need for hurrying, she waited until the picture was carefully taken out, rolled up, and carried safely away. Then she was ready to join her friends.

The White House was burned. So was the Capitol. The fires lighted the sky so that the red glare could be seen for miles and miles. It was a ruined city to

DOLLY MADISON

which Dolly returned, a few days later.

But she was never one to fret over what she couldn't help. She found a new house. Soon she had made it into a home.

It was a very happy home when the news of peace came. Its doors stood open wide. It was crowded with friends who had come to rejoice with Dolly and her husband. The servants joined in the gaiety, until one of them wrote, "Such another joyful time was not seen in all Washington."

So Dolly became famous. The soldiers marching home from the war cheered before her house.

It wasn't because of what she did. She was so busy taking care of people who were doing big and important things, she never had a chance to do them herself. She didn't expect people to think that *she* was wise or brave or smart. She was just helpful and friendly. And that was enough.

It was enough to make Dolly Madison one of the best-loved women in American history.

Adapted from *Dolly Madison, Quaker Girl*

Robert Fulton
Makes the Paddles Work

By Clara Ingram Judson

THE YEAR that Robert Fulton was fourteen, he went on his usual spring visit to his aunt in Little Britain Township, Pennsylvania. Mr. Isch, who owned the blacksmith shop in Lancaster where Robert worked after school, let him off from the shop, for he knew how important it was for the Fulton family to have the wool and maple sugar and meat which the boy would bring back.

Visiting his aunt meant doing a lot of hard work, of course, but it was fun for a change. His aunt loved him dearly and treated him as an honored guest. Often she gave him clothes and money for books, and always she listened eagerly to his talk.

"What will you draw tonight, Robert?" she asked as he opened his portfolio the first evening of his stay.

She loved watching him draw. It seemed like magic to see a plain piece of paper become a person or a scene or a pattern right before her eyes. Her fingers were skillful at knitting and weaving, sewing and spinning, but clumsy with a pencil. "Looks like you're making wheels. No, they aren't wheels either." She dropped her knitting and stared, fascinated.

"They are not wheels like on a cart, ma'am. This is a windlass and these things that look like wheels are really paddles." Robert put in more lines. "See, ma'am? These are the paddles I'm putting on now. They fasten on at the end. They will move a boat."

"Move a boat! Those? Without poling?"

"Yes. You turn the windlass here"—he pointed with his pencil. "The wheel moves here and the paddles turn through the water and the boat moves."

"Now you're funning me, nephew!" She laughed with easy good humor. "You can't move a boat with a picture!"

"No, not with a picture. But with real paddles made like the picture. As soon as I've finished the drawing, I'll make a model and you shall see it."

She picked up her knitting. No use wasting time, and she wanted to finish the jacket to send back to Robert's brother. But she watched carefully as she knitted and saw Robert finish the drawing. Then he gathered materials for the model, a board, some bits of wood, wire, and metal. Under her very eyes, the model took shape, not in one evening, but slowly, as Robert worked on it every spare minute.

The last day of his stay it was finished, and Robert gleefully tried it in the great rain barrel. It worked! He turned the small windlass and slowly, smoothly, the paddles went round and round. The boat moved! It ran into the side of the rain barrel in no time at all! His aunt could hardly believe her eyes and she watched eagerly as he adjusted this and that to make it perfect.

"It's a pretty toy," she admitted, "and you're a smart lad to make it. But don't get to thinking that a toy is like a real boat that

has to be poled."

"It's not a toy, ma'am." Robert lifted the model from the water and carefully wiped it dry. "I'll make a real scow work just as this does when I get home. But I could never carry this with all else I have to take with me. Anyway, I have this fixed in my mind. May I put it in the attic, ma'am? Have you room?"

"All the room you want, lad," his aunt told him cordially. "I'll take care that it's here for you next time you come. It *is* a pretty thing." She studied the little model, still puzzled by the way it worked. She little guessed that before many years passed, it would be brought down from the attic and set on the living-room mantel to be admired by visitors from near and far.

As soon as possible after his return home, Robert dashed off to tell his friend, Christopher Gumpf, about his model.

"I made it exactly like the drawing and it works, Chris! It works! We can try it on your father's scow when he goes fishing. We can go up or down the river, and it'll be no work at all."

"Don't you use a pole?" Christopher wondered.

"Oh, maybe we'll need to push off from shore. But we'll not

use a pole for pushing the boat. I promise you."

"Well, we shall see." Christopher did not sound very encouraging.

"That we shall," agreed Robert cheerfully. "And we'll not tell a person, not one, till it's done and tried out." Christopher was willing enough to promise that, because he did not like the thought of the teasing he would get when the thing failed.

The two boys collected planks and boards. Robert begged and bought scrap iron from Mr. Isch and worked evenings at the forge until he had made a crank and windlass, according to his design. They made matching paddles, by fastening stout, slender planks at right angles and mounting a crosspiece at each end. The crank was attached to the scow crosswise near the stern.

"Think how speedy a light boat would be," Robert said, as they fitted and hammered in the twilight. Dark would soon overtake them and he wanted to finish that evening. "This old thing is clumsy as an old cow. Let's make a new boat, Chris."

"If the paddles work, maybe we could."

"They'll work." Robert had no fears. "You tell your father

we'll go fishing about six, to-morrow. We've only to set the paddle wheels and we can do that in half an hour. I'll not bother about supper."

Next day Deter Gumpf, Christopher's father, was there at six, but the scow was gone. A sound up toward the bend caught his attention—what was that thing, coming downriver? A scow that looked for all the world like his, except for queer contraptions on each side, was coming toward him. Christopher was sitting at the stern. Robert was standing, turning something up and down, round and round.

"They work!" Christopher shouted when he spied his father. "The paddles work!"

Deter Gumpf stared, speechless. Had those boys ruined his scow?

Two boys who were setting squirrel traps also heard Christopher's shout. They pushed aside the bushes just in time to see the scow glide slowly toward the bank as Robert stopped turning the paddles. Mr. Gumpf stepped aboard.

"You see, sir," they heard Robert explain, "you turn this crank, and that moves the paddles—so. And the paddles move the boat. It's simple." Mr. Gumpf looked doubtful. "Want to try it?"

"No, you do it." Deter Gumpf preferred to sit. So Robert turned the crank and the scow moved along.

"Hi! Take us!" the boys shouted.

ROBERT FULTON

"Another time! Perhaps Mr. Gumpf will invite you," answered Robert. Then as an afterthought he added, "But if you ride, you have to take your turn at the windlass."

Robert's success was greater than he expected. He not only was relieved of poling but of cranking, too. The village boys were glad enough to take their turn at cranking for the excitement of going along. The wonder of that scow lasted all the summer. She was ceremoniously christened *George Washington.*

Robert enjoyed the success (and the easy fishing trips), but after the first evening his mind left the old scow far behind. If a hand-turned crank moved a boat, why wouldn't a steam engine do the task even better?

Night after night he turned the problem over in his mind, and, when Robert Fulton grew up, he did find a way to make a steam engine move a boat. He built the steamship *Clermont* and on August 17, 1807, he made a trip by steam up the Hudson River from New York City to Albany.

Many an evening, as his family sat before the sitting-room fire, his children would beg for stories of his boyhood. Their favorite story was the one about the boat with paddles.

"You called it the *George Washington,* didn't you, Father?" young Robert asked. "Was it hard to turn the paddles?"

"Yes, it was hard—but easier than poling, at that!" his father answered. "And boys always wanted to do that job!"

"I wish I'd lived then!" Small Robert's eyes sparkled as he stood on the hearthrug and stared at his father adoringly.

"Don't say that, son!" Robert Fulton exclaimed. "You live at a better time! And, some day, maybe you'll see a steamboat cross the ocean!"

"*Really,* Father? You think of wonderful things!" the children said.

Adapted from *Boat Builder*

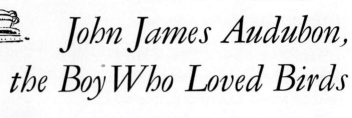

John James Audubon, the Boy Who Loved Birds

By Carolyn Sherwin Bailey

JOHN AUDUBON had a stepmother who loved him so much that she came close to spoiling him. The family lived in the small town of Nantes in the Loire Valley of France. John and his father had been travelers nearly all of John's ten years. Santo Domingo, with its jungles, clipper ships, spices, and coffee plantations; New Orleans with its beautiful gardens; sailing ships that crossed the Atlantic Ocean with cargoes of tea, indigo, and silks; France in the period of 1790—all these had been experienced by the boy, because his father was a trader. But when we see John first, he is in the breakfast room of the house in Nantes, and with him is Mignonne, his pet parrot.

Mignonne was a wiser parrot than most. Perched on the back of John's chair she plumed her gold and green feathers and talked in French. She always had her breakfast with the boy, and that morning she ordered in her sharp voice, warm milk, a roll, and some sugar. John's good stepmother hurried in with the breakfast tray, but before she could set it down a flying ball of fur dropped from the top of a chest of drawers in the corner of the room. Before either the boy or his mother could do anything, John's pet monkey, who had also been waiting for breakfast, had caught poor Mignonne about the neck and choked her to death.

This is a sad way to begin a story, but Mignonne's death started

60

JOHN JAMES AUDUBON

a deep love of birds in John's heart. When his jealous little monkey killed Mignonne in a fit of temper, John made up his mind that no other bird should die if he could help it.

At this time Mr. Audubon, John's father, was away at sea. Before sailing, he had entered John in a day school in Nantes, where he would be taught the lessons that were thought best for a boy in those days: drawing, arithmetic, geography, music, and fencing. John loved his drawing lessons, and soon showed that he could paint and sketch better than any of his classmates. But he liked to escape from his hard school bench into the forest and follow the banks of the River Loire, looking for birds. When he wanted to spend a day in the woods watching the ways of birds and rabbits, his mother packed a large basket of lunch for him. Soon his room looked like a museum. The walls were covered with paintings of birds, and the shelves with birds' nests. All the drawers held birds' eggs, pressed flowers, and pebbles, each one carefully labeled. John was teaching himself to be a naturalist, but this helped him very little in his school work. And after awhile his father came home from his sea trip.

On his first evening at home, Mr. Audubon called John and his sister into the drawing room to test them in their school work. The little girl played a piece on the piano without the music notes.

She read some French stories, repeated the arithmetic tables, and danced all the figures of a minuet. But, alas, John failed in everything that he should have been learning at school. His father did not scold him, but the next morning John's trunk was packed and his father took him in a carriage to the depot where horses for Paris were waiting. John James Audubon was sent to a boarding school, far away from the forests of Nantes.

The change, though, was for the better. The lessons John had at his new school helped him in his study of outdoors. Geography taught him how climate controls the growth of plants and flowers, how it affects the habits of birds and animals. Painting was added to drawing. John Audubon made two hundred drawings and paintings of birds and animals before he was sixteen years old, and his school marks were so high that his father gave the boy a trip to America as a reward.

Mr. Audubon had a business friend in the United States, Miles Fisher, the Quaker. Mr. Fisher owned Mill-Grove Farm, not far from the city of Philadelphia, a place of wide fields, avenues of trees, thick orchards, an old mill, and a delightful cave in which the peewees built their nests and sang. There Mr. Audubon left John. Mill-Grove Farm was almost as pleasant a place as Nantes, but its only drawback in John Audubon's eyes was the stern rule of Mr. Fisher. After what he considered a sufficient vacation, he sent John to school, had him work on the farm every day after school, and allowed him to spend only his spare time studying nature.

John thought of running away, but one day he met Lucy Bakewell, who lived on the next farm. Lucy was an outdoor girl and loved birds and flowers almost as dearly as John did. Together they skated in the winter and had picnics in the summer. John watched and listened to one bird every day, learning its song, nesting ways, and coloring. Lucy helped him with the school work

JOHN JAMES AUDUBON

that he disliked, and John taught
Lucy how to paint and draw.
When John's schooling was over,
he decided to go out West, where
the plains were covered with different kinds of flowers, and there
were strange birds and animals
to study. Lucy Bakewell promised to take care of John's collection of birds' nests, eggs, and
drawings, and wait for his return.

That was the beginning of
John James Audubon's adventurous life. He traveled through the
entire United States, walking, riding horseback, following the
rivers in a flatboat. After awhile he came back to Mill-Grove Farm
and married Lucy. They went West and opened a general store in
Louisville, Kentucky.

But John Audubon found standing behind a store counter as
tiresome as school had been. He made his way to the Mississippi
Valley to study water birds. After that he found work in the new
museum of Cincinnati, stuffing and arranging the museum's collection of birds. Soon he traveled on again, always following bird
and animal life and making such paintings of them as the world
had never known.

Sometimes April 26, the birthday of John James Audubon,
is celebrated as Bird Day. But he liked children to keep every day
as Bird Day—a time for watching and loving one bird, one small
wild creature, or one flower. Because of his story which began with
Mignonne, the parrot, boys and girls all over our land and in foreign
countries as well have banded together to keep wild birds safe and
happy.

Adapted from *Tell Me a Birthday Story*

A New, Bright World for Jenny Lind

By Laura Benét

"NOW PUSSY, Askade (beloved), you shall hear this tune. Sit still, Pussy, my child, and don't leap about so. Come now."

A pale-cheeked, plain little girl spoke from the window sill of the steward's room at the Widows' House in Stockholm, Sweden. Seated beside her was a big, handsome cat with a blue ribbon round its neck, purring violently. The cat's mistress threw back her head and there poured into the plainly furnished room a song—clear, sweet, and golden as sunlight.

Pussy looked gratified, blinked one eye, and promptly went to sleep. Jenny drew the furry ball into her lap and began to sing again. The room in which they sat alone had the usual big, air-tight stove, brightly painted wooden chairs, and gay coverings.

A NEW, BRIGHT WORLD FOR JENNY LIND

Swedish folk like color in their homes, as well as music. It was here that Jenny Lind had come, because of family difficulties, to live with her beloved grandmother.

The window, Jenny's favorite, looked out on the street leading up to St. Jacob's Church. Today the street was full of vehicles, as well as people passing on foot. Jenny did not notice various persons who stopped to listen to her singing. Young men began to hum in response. Farmers, who had come into the city to buy and sell, stood stock-still, tears welling into their eyes. Or some young banker's clerk, hurrying by, said to himself, "Oh for a sweetheart who could sing like that. One might then never feel tired."

But the little girl, Jenny Lind, was not aware of their thoughts. It was September, 1829, and in a week or two she would be nine years old. The past year at the Widows' House had been the happiest of her unhappy childhood.

Downstairs lived the caretaker couple, kindly folk who asked no particular tasks of her. Upstairs were her pious, devoted grandmother and the other widows in their caps and kerchiefs who sat for the most part doing needlework or spinning at their wheels. Often they would teach her some pretty needlework stitch or help to make a dress for her. Good Fru (Mrs.) Tengmark, her grandmother, looked after her religious training. Though she was homely, poor and without playthings, Jenny's joy came from within herself. Her music was as much a part of her as eyes or hands.

That afternoon Jenny's mother arrived to see how she and her grandmother were getting along. The three of them had much to say to one another. They were having a treat of coffee and cakes when a sudden knock came upon the door.

"Come in," they answered, thinking it was the matron.

The visitor entered, a young servant girl, neatly dressed, who curtsied as she came up to them.

"Good day, ladies," she began. "I come from Mademoiselle Lundberg, who is a performer at the Royal Opera House. I often pass this window on errands for my mistress, and have ventured to tell her that I never heard such beautiful music as this little girl"—and she nodded in Jenny's direction—"sings to her cat. Mademoiselle Lundberg is so much interested that she has sent me to request you, Fru, to bring your daughter to sing to her tomorrow."

Fru Lind, amazed, felt greatly flattered and replied, "Thank your mistress and tell her we will come tomorrow afternoon if that will suit her plans." And Fru Tengmark added, "Yes, go by all means, daughter. Who knows to what this may lead?"

Nine-year-old Jenny heard the words as in a dream. What was one song, more or less, to her whose singing was her breath?

The next day Jenny and her mother went to see Mademoiselle Lundberg in her comfortable lodgings. "You will sing for me, will you not, little one?" she said.

Jenny curtsied and began one of her childhood songs. Mademoiselle Lundberg sat quite still when she had finished. Then she turned to Fru Lind. "This child is a genius!" she exclaimed. "Oh, Madame, you must have her educated for the stage."

Fru Lind drew herself up haughtily. "The stage! I could never consent to such a thing. What a life for a little girl!"

Jenny kept quiet, but her cheeks grew hot with excitement. Mademoiselle Lundberg was aware that she had said the wrong thing. "At least, you must have her taught singing," she pleaded. "It is not once in years that one hears such a voice. I will give you a letter of introduction to Herr Croelius. He is the Singing Master at the Royal Theater. You will take your daughter to him, will you not? I beg that you will."

Persuasion at first bore no fruit. But when Fru Lind finally left, she carried with her a letter from Mademoiselle Lundberg. Mother and daughter then set forth for the Royal Opera House, a large and handsome gray building. The airy rooms of its second story housed the School of Girls, and this theater was supported by the Government.

After a little delay the visitors were shown into a room where Herr Croelius sat in his black frock coat. His eyes were understanding, and Jenny thought, "I shall not be afraid of him, no matter what Mama says."

Then a deep, kindly voice was speaking, asking her to sing. Again Jenny stood and sang, this time an air from one of the operas. She sang it fully and freely. It was easy to sing. With this master there was nothing to fear.

When she had finished, Herr Croelius turned to her mother, "I must take her in to see Count Puke, the head of the theater. I shall lose no time in telling him what a treasure I have discovered." Herr Croelius was wiping his eyes with a handkerchief. That was funny.

Fru Lind was left waiting in his office while Jenny went with

him to the Count. But the great man greeted them grimly.

"How old is this girl?" he asked.

"Nine years old, Count."

"Only nine? But this place is not a crèche (nursery). It is the King's theater." He looked intently down his long nose at quiet little Jenny. "Why, she is undersized, awkward, and quite plain! What could I do with such an ugly little girl?"

Herr Croelius put an arm protectingly about the child. Jenny stood looking at the floor, wishing she might fall through it.

After a pause, Herr Croelius collected himself and said calmly, "If you will not hear her, Count, I will teach her myself. And one day she will astonish you!"

"Let me hear her, then," growled the Count.

Jenny sang. As that childish voice mounted in purity and strength, a change came over his dour expression. Then he spoke: "Accept the girl for the Royal Theater School. She shall be taught to sing and educated at the Government's expense."

Already Jenny knew in her heart that she would like to come here to work and learn. The vista of a new and bright world opened before her. She would do great things.

From *Enchanting Jenny Lind*

Abraham Lincoln's Boyhood

As Told by Himself

FEBRUARY 12, 1809. I was born February 12, 1809, near where Hogginsville (Hodgenville) now is, in Kentucky. My parents were both born in Virginia. My mother, who died in my tenth year, was of a family of the name of Hanks. My grandfather, Abraham Lincoln, came from Virginia to Kentucky about 1781 or 1782. A year or two later he was killed by the Indians, when he was laboring to open a farm in the forest. My father, at the death of his father, was but six years of age, and he grew up without education. Even in childhood he was a wandering laboring-boy, and never did more in the way of writing than to write his own name.

1813. Thomas Lincoln takes a farm on Knob Creek, Kentucky. The place on Knob Creek I remember very well. My earliest memory is of the Knob Creek place.

1814. Before leaving Kentucky, I and my sister were sent, for short periods, to A B C schools.

1815. With weapons no more formidable than hickory clubs, Austin Gallaher and I had been playing in the woods and hunting rabbits. After several hours of vigorous exercise we had stopped to rest. After a while I threw down my cap, climbed a tree, and was resting comfortably in the forks of two limbs.

Below me, stretched out full length on the grass, was Austin apparently asleep. Beside him lay his cap, the inside facing upward. In the pocket of my little jacket reposed a pawpaw which I had found shortly before. The thought suddenly occurred to me that it would be great fun to drop it into Austin's upturned cap.

The pawpaw was so ripe and soft I could scarcely withdraw it whole from my pocket. Taking careful aim, I let it fall. I had calculated just right, for it struck the cap center and I could see portions of soft yellow pawpaw spattering in every direction. I paused to observe the result, convinced that Austin would be angry but, strange to relate, what I had done failed to arouse him.

Presently I slid down the tree. Imagine my surprise when I reached the ground and learned that, instead of sleeping, Austin had really been awake. While I was climbing the tree he had cleverly changed caps, substituting my own for his. So, instead of tormenting him as I had intended, I had simply besmeared my own headgear.

1816. Our farm was composed of three fields which lay in the valley surrounded by high hills and deep gorges. Sometimes when there came a big rain in the hills, the water would come down the gorges and spread over the farm. The last thing I remember doing there was on a Saturday afternoon. The other boys planted the corn in what we called the "big field"—it contained seven acres— and I dropped the pumpkin seed. I dropped two seeds every other hill and every other row. The next Sunday morning there came a big rain in the hills. It did not rain a drop in the valley, but the water, coming down through the gorges, washed ground, corn, pumpkin seeds, and all clear off the field.

I can remember our life in Kentucky: the cabin, the hard way of living, the sale of our possessions, and the journey with my father and mother to southern Indiana. We moved to what is now Spencer County, Indiana, in my eighth year.

Autumn, 1816. Thomas Lincoln and his family settle on uncleared land, near Pigeon Creek, not far from Rockport, Indiana. We settled in an unbroken forest, and the clearing away of surplus wood was the great task ahead. I was large for my age, and had an ax put into my hands at once. From that time until my twenty-third year I was almost constantly handling that most useful instrument.

February, 1817. Our new home was a wild region with many bears and other wild animals still in the woods. There I made an early start as a hunter, which was never much improved afterward. A few days before the end of my eighth year, in the absence of my father, a flock of wild turkeys approached the new log cabin. I was standing inside, with rifle-gun, and shot through a crack and killed one of them. I have never since pulled a trigger on any larger game.

It was pretty pinching times at first in Indiana, getting the cabin built, and clearing for the crops, but presently we got reasonably comfortable.

October 5, 1818. My mother died.

1819. I was kicked by a horse and apparently dead for a time.

December 2. My father married Mrs. Sally Johnston, a widow with three children, at Elizabethtown, Kentucky. She proved a good and kind mother to me.

1820. There were some schools, so called, but nothing was ever required of a teacher beyond "readin', writin', and cipherin'" to the rule of three. If a straggler supposed to understand Latin happened to stop in the neighborhood, he was looked upon as a wizard. I went to A B C schools by littles. I now think that all my schooling did not amount to one year.

(In a copy book):

Abraham Lincoln, his hand and pen,

He will be good, but God knows when.

1821 (?). Among my earliest memories, I remember how, when a mere child, I used to get irritated when anybody talked to me in a way that I could not understand. I can remember going to my little bedroom, after hearing the neighbors talk of an evening with my father. I would spend a large part of the night trying to make out the exact meaning of what they had said.

ABRAHAM LINCOLN'S BOYHOOD

I could not sleep, when I got on such a hunt for an idea, until I had caught it. When I thought I had got it, I was not satisfied until I had repeated it over and over again. I had to put it in language plain enough, as I thought, for any boy I knew to understand.

One day a wagon broke down near us. In it were a lady and two girls and a man, and while they were fixing up, they cooked in our kitchen. The woman had books and read us stories. I took a great fancy to one of the girls, and when they were gone I thought of her a great deal.

One day, when I was sitting out in the sun by the house, I wrote out a story in my mind. I thought I took my father's horse and followed the wagon, and finally I found it. I talked with the girl and persuaded her to elope with me. That night I put her on my horse, and we started off across the prairie. After several hours we came to a camp; and when we rode up we found it was the one we had left a few hours before, and we went in. The next night we tried again, and the same thing happened. The horse came back to the same place; and then we decided that we ought not to elope. I stayed until I had persuaded her father to give her to me. I always meant to write that story out and publish it. I began once, but I decided that it was not much of a story. But I think that was the beginning of love with me.

Away back in my childhood, the earliest days of my being able to read, I got hold of a small book, Weems' *Life of Washington*. I remember reading in it about the battlefields and struggles for the liberties of the country. None fixed themselves upon my imagination so deeply as the struggle at Trenton, New Jersey. The crossing of the river, the contest with the Hessians, the great hardships endured at that time, all fixed themselves on my memory more than any single event of the Revolution. I remember thinking then, boy even though I was, that there must have been something more than common that these men struggled for.

1824. I was raised to farm work till I was twenty-two.

1827. He undertakes to run a ferry across the Ohio, sixteen miles from home. I was contemplating a new flatboat, and wondering whether I could make it stronger or improve it in any way. Two men came down to the shore in carriages with trunks. After looking at the different boats, they singled out mine, and asked, "Who owns this?"

I answered, somewhat modestly, "I do."

"Will you," said one of them, "take us to the steamer?"

"Certainly," said I. I was glad to have the chance of earning something. I supposed that each of them would give me two or three bits. The trunks were put on my flatboat, and the passengers seated themselves on the trunks, and I sculled them out to the steamer.

They got on board, and I lifted up their heavy trunks and put them on deck. The steamer was about to put on steam again, when I called out that they had forgotten to pay me. Each of them took from his pocket a silver half dollar and threw it on the floor of my boat. I could scarcely believe my eyes as I picked up the money. I could scarcely credit that I, a poor boy, had earned a dollar in less than a day. The world seemed fairer and wider before me. I was a more hopeful and confident being from that hour.

Adapted from *An Autobiography of Abraham Lincoln,* compiled by N. W. Stephenson

Louisa Alcott's Childhood

By Louisa May Alcott

ONE of my earliest memories is of playing with books in my
father's study, building houses and bridges of the big dic-
tionaries and diaries, looking at pictures, pretending to
read, and scribbling on blank pages whenever pen or pencil could
be found.

On one occasion my older sister, Anna, and I built a high tower
round baby Lizzie as she sat playing with her toys on the floor.
Then, being attracted by something out-of-doors, we forgot our
little prisoner. A search was made, and patient baby was at last
discovered curled up and fast asleep in her dungeon cell. But she
emerged so rosy and smiling after her nap, that we were forgiven

for our carelessness.

Another memory is of my fourth birthday, which was celebrated at my father's schoolroom in Masonic Temple in Boston.
All the children were there. I wore a crown of flowers, and stood
upon a table to give out cakes to each child as the procession
marched past. By some oversight the cakes fell short, and I saw
that if I gave away the last one *I* should have none. As I was queen
of the party, I felt that I ought to have it. I held on to it tightly till
my mother said,

"It is always better to give away than to keep the nice things;
so I know my Louy will not let the little friend go without."

The little friend received that dear plummy cake, and I a kiss
and my first lesson in the sweetness of self-denial, a lesson which
my dear mother beautifully illustrated all her long life.

Running away was one of the delights of my early days. I still
enjoy sudden flights out of the home nest to look about this very
interesting world, and then go back to report.

On one of these occasions I passed a varied day with some Irish
children, who hospitably shared their cold potatoes, salt-fish, and
crusts with me. We reveled in the ash heaps which then adorned
the waste lands where the Albany Depot now stands. A trip to the
Boston Common cheered the afternoon, but as dusk set in my
friends deserted me.

I felt that home was a nice place after all, and tried to find it. I
dimly remember watching a lamplighter as I sat to rest on some
doorsteps in Bedford Street. A big dog welcomed me so kindly
that I fell asleep with my head pillowed on his curly back, and was
found there by the town crier, whom my distracted parents had
sent in search of me. His bell and proclamation of the loss of "a
little girl, six years old, in a pink frock, white hat, and new green
shoes," woke me up, and a small voice answered out of the darkness,

"Why, dat's me!"

LOUISA ALCOTT'S CHILDHOOD

Being with difficulty torn from my four-footed friend, I was carried to the crier's house, and there feasted on bread-and-molasses in a tin plate. But my fun ended next day when I was tied to the arm of the sofa to repent at leisure.

I never went to school except to my father or such governesses as from time to time came into the family. Schools then were not what they are now; so we had lessons each morning in the study. And very happy hours they were to us, for my father was a very wise teacher. I never liked arithmetic or grammar; but reading, writing, composition, history, and geography I enjoyed, as well as the stories he read to us.

Pilgrim's Progress and the best of the dear old fairy tales made the reading hour the pleasantest of our day. On Sundays we had a simple service of Bible stories, hymns, and conversation about the state of our little consciences and the conduct of our childish lives which never will be forgotten.

Walks each morning around the Common while in the city, and long tramps over hill and dale when our home was in the country, were a part of our education. We learned every sort of housework, for which I have always been very grateful. Needlework began early, and at ten my skillful sister made a linen shirt beautifully. At twelve I set up as a doll's dressmaker, with my sign out and wonderful models in my window. All the children employed me, and my turbans were the rage at one time, to the great dismay of the neighbor's hens. These were hotly hunted down, that I might tweak out their downiest feathers to adorn the dolls' headgear.

Active exercise was my delight. When a child of six I drove my hoop round the Common without stopping. It was such a joy to run. No boy could be my friend till I had beaten him in a race, and no girl if she refused to climb trees, leap fences, and be a tomboy.

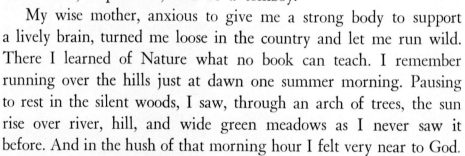

My wise mother, anxious to give me a strong body to support a lively brain, turned me loose in the country and let me run wild. There I learned of Nature what no book can teach. I remember running over the hills just at dawn one summer morning. Pausing to rest in the silent woods, I saw, through an arch of trees, the sun rise over river, hill, and wide green meadows as I never saw it before. And in the hush of that morning hour I felt very near to God.

The days which we spent in the town of Concord were the happiest of my life. We had charming playmates in the little Emersons, Channings, Hawthornes, and Goodwins, with their famous parents and their friends to enjoy our pranks and share our fun.

Plays in the barn were a favorite amusement, and we dramatized the fairy tales in great style. Our giant came tumbling off a loft when Jack cut down the squash-vine running up a ladder to represent the immortal bean. Cinderella rolled away in a vast pumpkin.

And a long black pudding was lowered by invisible hands to fasten itself on the nose of the man who wasted his three wishes.

Pilgrims journeyed over the hill with their staffs and cockle-shells in their hats. Fairies held their pretty revels among the whispering birches. Strawberry parties in the rustic arbor were honored by poets and philosophers, who fed us on their wit and wisdom while the little girls served us more mortal food.

(*Note:* When Louisa Alcott grew up she wrote *Little Women* about the experiences of her own family in the town of Concord, Massachusetts. The "Jo" of the story was Louisa herself; "Meg" was her older sister, Anna; and "Beth" was Elizabeth, the "baby Lizzie" mentioned above. Another little girl, Abba May, was born later, and in *Little Women* was called "Amy.")

Adapted from "Sketch of Childhood, by Herself," in *Louisa May Alcott: Her Life, Letters and Journals.*

The Story of Robert E. Lee

By Smith Burnham

ROBERT E. LEE'S father, Colonel Henry Lee, was a hero of the Revolutionary War. He was called "Light-Horse Harry" because he was so ready and alert with his cavalry regiment. He was such a friend of the commander-in-chief that it was said, "General Washington loves Harry Lee as if he were his own son."

Robert Lee was born in Virginia, near the Potomac River, in a huge brick house which looked like a mansion, a castle, and a fort, all in one. When he was four, his father moved to Alexandria, near the new city of Washington, to send the boy and his brothers and sisters to school.

The father died when Robert was eleven, and his mother was an invalid. The oldest Lee son was in Harvard College, and the next was a midshipman in the Naval Academy at Annapolis. So Robert was left at home to take care of his mother. Whenever she was well enough to go for a drive, he carried her out to the family coach in his strong arms.

Feeling that his mother could not afford to send him to college, young Robert studied hard to enter West Point Military Academy. No mother ever had more reason to be proud of her tall, handsome son.

"How can I do without Robert?" she said. "He is both son and daughter to me!"

THE STORY OF ROBERT E. LEE

Robert became a West Point cadet at eighteen. Young Jefferson Davis, who was there at the same time, fell off a cliff and nearly lost his life while breaking the rules of the Academy. Young Ulysses Grant wrote home ten years later that it was impossible to get through at West Point without "black marks," or demerits. But Robert E. Lee went through the whole four years without a single black mark! He had come to West Point, at his country's expense, to learn to be a soldier. And he believed that the first duty of a soldier was to obey.

It was a wonder that the other cadets did not hate a young man who seemed to feel that he must behave better than the rest of them. But he was so kind that they never called him a "goody-goody boy" or a prig. At graduation, Lieutenant Lee was the most popular man at West Point; and he ranked second in his class.

Lee's courage was put to the test in the Mexican War. On a dark night he found the way across a dangerous lava field cracked in all directions by deep crevices—"without light, without a companion or guide, where scarcely a step could be taken without fear of death." General Scott, then chief in command, said this was the bravest act performed by any one during the campaign.

When the War between the States broke out, President Lincoln offered Colonel Lee the

highest command of the United States Army. But Colonel Lee did not accept the honor. He did not believe in slavery, and did not think it was right for any of the states to secede, or leave the Union. But he was a Virginian, and he could not bring himself to lead an army against his relatives, friends, and neighbors. He had heard his father, who was once governor of the state, say with deepest feeling, "Virginia is my country; her will I obey, no matter how sad my fate may be." So, when his native state went out of the Union, Robert E. Lee resigned as colonel in the United States Army and went with her.

General Lee soon proved that he was a great general. With smaller armies and poorer supplies and weapons than those of the North, he gained many victories. He defeated four Northern generals, one after another. It took Grant, the sixth general sent against him, a whole year to surround Lee's army.

So noble and dignified was General Lee's character that he was honored and admired by North and South alike.

From *Hero Tales from History*

Clara Barton, the Young Schoolteacher

By Mildred Mastin Pace

CLARA BARTON was getting over the mumps, and this was her first day downstairs. She lay on the couch in the darkened living room and half listened to the sound of voices that drifted from the front parlor. Her parents were entertaining a well-known scientist, and while Clara knew the talk was undoubtedly interesting and instructive, she felt too lazy and contented to take an active part in it.

But when she heard her name mentioned, she listened more carefully. Her mother was saying to the guest, "You are a brilliant man. Tell me what I can do about our Clara. She is so shy and frightened among strangers, and even with us she is timid."

Clara felt miserable to think she caused her parents such deep concern. She waited anxiously for the great man's answer. He said,

CLARA BARTON

"Throw responsibility on her. Get her a school to teach—"

Clara was only fifteen, small and childish for her age. But having received the scientist's advice, Mrs. Barton intended to follow it. Shortly after his visit it was arranged for Clara to teach spring term at the near-by district schoolhouse.

What a time the Bartons had trying to make Clara look grown up! Dorothy and Sally, her older sisters, combed out her braids and experimented with ladylike hair arrangements until they found one they thought suited.

"We fixed it high on your head to make you look taller," Sally explained. "You really are little."

Clara thought she looked very funny with her hair put up. Then her mother came with the new dress she had made. It was long and bulky, to make a small girl look bigger. Clara took off the little-girl dress and put on the new one. She felt exactly as if she were dressed up in her mother's clothes!

It was a bright May morning when Clara started out, alone and excited, to begin her first term as a teacher. The schoolhouse was a square, one-room building of stone, and it was spilling over with forty pupils, all on time for the first day of the new term.

The children ranged from the little four-year-olds on up to a group of boys as old as Clara and much larger than she. She had been warned about these boys. They were known troublemakers. Just the year before they had decided they didn't like the new teacher and had taken charge themselves—putting the poor creature out by force.

But Clara didn't have time to worry about them just then. She was worried about herself. Forty pairs of eyes watched her curiously, and she was timid and inexperienced. Besides, having gone to public school so seldom herself, she didn't know just how to open a school on the first day. Should she make a little speech, or should she begin right off with lessons? Was the teacher supposed to introduce herself? She wished she had asked Dorothy.

Before her, on her desk, was a Bible. She knew she could never make a speech, but she could read. So she told the children to take their Testaments out of their desks and turn to the Sermon on the Mount. She saw a smirk cross the face of one of the biggest boys. But the room was very quiet as Clara read the first verse. Then each child who had learned to read was called upon in turn. The beautiful dignity of the words filled the little school, and even the biggest boys became sober and attentive.

As the children spoke the familiar verses, they suddenly ceased to be strangers to Clara. When the Sermon was ended, she was no longer afraid of them. With an ease that surprised her, she turned to the work of classing the children, planning lessons and assignments.

Clara knew, however, that sooner or later she would have trouble with the big boys. It came before long.

The trouble started on the playground. The older group was playing a game of ball, and instead of confining their game to the field, they took delight in running out of bounds, into the yard where the smaller children played. Several younger children were knocked down, and ran crying to Clara. This brought guffaws from the big boys, and the game continued in its rough and

dangerous way.

Clara knew all the rules of their game. David, her big brother, had taught her to play it. She walked quietly out onto the playing field, and said, "Boys, I don't think you know how to play this game. At least you're not following the rules. May I show you?"

There was a snicker all around as the tiny teacher picked up the ball. With a few quick instructions she sent the other players to their places, and the game began.

Within five minutes the boys' eyes were wide with surprise and admiration. Here was a girl their own age, and as swift and agile as they! Not one could throw as true as she could, nor as far. She could beat them at their own game!

When playtime was over, Clara dusted herself off and went into the schoolhouse to ring the bell. She had no further worry about the big boys. And how she blessed David for his lessons!

The "troublemakers" were now Clara's allies. They thought she was the most remarkable girl they had ever known. When the big boys showed themselves so eager to co-operate with her, the younger children naturally followed their example. Soon the school was running so smoothly, Clara laughed at the fears that had haunted her that first terrible day.

It was a happy school. Clara played with the children, and all the children worked with Clara. And when the last day of the term came, the teacher realized it was far harder than the first day had been. It meant saying good-by. Clara had done so well with the little one-room school that she had been offered a better position.

A few days later, at Town Meeting, it was announced that Clara's school, of all the schools in that section, had been voted first in discipline. Tears came to Clara's eyes and she protested, "We had no discipline. We were all just happy together. No child was ever scolded or punished. Please don't give my school the discipline award." But the grown-ups just smiled, and thought the girl teacher was being modest.

Each year Clara was offered a better school, and each year her reputation grew as a kind and efficient teacher. Finally she travelled to Bordentown, New Jersey, to take charge of a school that badly needed a good teacher. At that time there were few public schools west of New York, and the Bordentown school, like most others, charged a fee. The children had to pay to attend.

In Bordentown, Clara found few children in her schoolroom, but many youngsters running the streets. One day she stopped a wild little group and asked them why they didn't go to school.

"We'd like to go to school, lady," one boy said, "but there is no school for us. We can't pay the fee."

"You shall have a school," Clara promised them.

When the people of Bordentown heard that she planned to open the school to the street children, they were horrified!

"Those children are ruffians—they should be locked up, not sent to school," some exclaimed.

"What kind of a woman is this new teacher, to consider working with boys of that sort? She can't be respectable!" others cried.

"Nice children can't go to school with those little hoodlums. . . . She'll soon find no woman can handle them. . . ." The protests and accusations rumbled. But Clara's ears were deaf to them.

"They aren't bad children," she said quietly. "I've talked with them. They are eager to learn. But if you leave them on the streets, they'll become bad."

"I want no salary," she explained to the school board. "I'll teach for nothing. All I want is your recognition and approval."

Finally she won her argument, and the school doors were opened to all the children. It was a hard job and a big one she tackled. But the Bordentown school grew, and after the first year she had to have more room and an assistant. It was a great victory.

In the years to come Clara Barton was to win many victories for humanity. During the War between the States, she nursed the soldiers at the front and became known as the "Angel of the Battlefield." Later she founded the American Red Cross.

From *Clara Barton*

When Mark Twain Was a Boy

By Margaret Ford Allen

THIS is the story of the real Tom Sawyer, a boy who grew up to be a famous writer. He was born more than a hundred years ago in a little cabin in Missouri. He never went to school after he was eleven years old, and he never saw a railroad until he was almost grown. If you had met him as a boy, roaming the woods barefooted with Huckleberry Finn (whose true name was Tom Blankenship), and if you had told him that one day he would become a famous writer and put himself and his chum into a book, which boys ever after would read, he would have stared at you. Huckleberry Finn would have stared at you. They would have said that you were telling a "stretcher."

The real Tom Sawyer came to live in the little white town of Hannibal, Missouri, when he was four years old. He came in a wagon, surrounded by furniture and all the worldly goods of the Clemens family. For his true name was not Tom Sawyer but Samuel Clemens. A wild, mischievous boy he was—small for his age, with a large head and thick hair which he had to brush continually if he kept it from curling. Sam was more of a trial, his mother often said, than all the other children put together.

If you have read *Tom Sawyer* and remember Aunt Polly, you will know just what Sam's mother was like. Aunt Polly in that book was Mrs. Clemens—a woman stern and at the same time so tender-hearted that she used to punish the cat for catching mice. The father was a poor and struggling lawyer who had wandered from town to town with his large family looking for better fortune, but had never quite succeeded in making both ends meet.

Afterward Sam always remembered Hannibal as a "white town drowsing in the sunshine of a summer morning." As a playground it could not have been improved. It looked out over the wide Mississippi River where one might watch puffing steamboats stopping to let off freight and passengers. Two miles or so below the town there was a wonderful cave, full of winding passages. And north of the town, a daring swim's distance, there was an island, three miles long and uninhabited, where boys could hunt turtle eggs to their hearts' content and build a fire and talk.

MARK TWAIN

Of all the boys in Hannibal, Sam especially admired a ragamuffin, dressed in fluttering patches, named Tom Blankenship. (This, of course, was Huckleberry Finn.) He was the only boy in the town who didn't have to go to school, or even church. He could sleep anywhere he chose —in an empty hogshed, if it suited him—and he didn't have to obey a single soul. All the mothers in town hated Tom Blankenship, and all the boys wanted to be like him. As for Sam, he adopted Tom on sight.

Many an evening he would leave his bed in answer to a faint "meow" from below. Out of the window he would climb to the roof of the shed beneath, and go down a trellis to join Tom Blankenship. Then they would set off together in search of some adventure. Usually John Briggs went with them—a boy whom you will remember as Joe Harper in the story of *Tom Sawyer*. You remember, too, that when the boys played pirate, Joe was called "The Terror of the Seas." Huckleberry Finn (that is, Tom Blankenship) was known as "The Red-handed."

One night Tom Blankenship had a dream. He dreamed that a chest of gold was buried near Hannibal. When Sam and John Briggs heard about it, they were excited and bargained for a share in the treasure in return for helping Tom dig. Armed with a pick and shovel, the boys set out through the woods. When they reached the spot, Tom Blankenship sat down under the shade of a pawpaw bush and gave directions, while Sam and John dug mightily. Tom wasn't expected to do any digging; he had had the dream and that was his share.

The real treasure hunt did not turn out as well as the one in the book, where Huck and Tom Sawyer finally located the box of gold in the haunted house. By late afternoon the real treasure hunters had about given up hope. Though they had laid bare many holes, they had not unearthed anything but an endless number of rocks. It was a hot day and Sam was almost exhausted. At last he threw down his shovel and vowed that his days of treasure hunting were over.

The adventures of Sam and his gang would have filled many books. You remember, in the tale of Tom Sawyer, how that hero saved Becky Thatcher from a whipping in school by taking the blame for something he did not do? Tom's sweetheart, Becky Thatcher, was a real little girl—Laura Hawkins, by name—a neighbor and playmate of Sam's in Hannibal. Whether or not he saved her from a whipping is not recorded. It is remembered, however, that once in a school spelling bee Sam did leave the "r" out of "February," on purpose, so that he would lose and she could win the medal. Sam was a poor pupil in most subjects, but he could spell. There was scarcely a week he did not wear the medal for the best speller in school. And Sam could always be counted on to be kindhearted and brave.

Mr. Cross's school in Hannibal, which Sam attended, stood on the Square in the center of town. There were two long benches on opposite sides of the schoolroom—one for the girls and the other on which all the boys sat. Up in front at a pine desk sat Mr. Cross, the teacher, who kept order—with the aid of a hickory stick.

It was here that the future author, biting his slate pencil, composed his first poem. When he had finished, he shoved his slate over to John Briggs, "the Terror of the Seas."

John snickered as he read:

"Cross by name and Cross by nature,
"Cross jumped over an Irish potato."

"Write it on the blackboard this noon, Sam," he begged. And when Sam refused, he added, "Why I wouldn't be ascairt to do it!"

"I dare you to!" hissed Sam.

"The Terror of the Seas" prided himself on never refusing a dare. When the pupils and teacher returned to school from their noontime meal, there in large round letters on the blackboard was the rhyme.

A titter went up from all the pupils, and suddenly Mr. Cross's eyes were peering straight into John Briggs'. He had recognized the handwriting. The teacher arose, stick in hand, and John paid with aching shoulders for Sam's first attempt at literature.

During the summertime, Sam Clemens, John Briggs, and Tom Blankenship played pirate in the cave down the river. It was a favorite pastime for Sunday School picnickers to explore that part of the cave near the known door. But Sam possessed a secret entrance of his own, which led to an unused section of this mazelike cavern. The would-be pirates climbed up to a thick clump of bushes which covered a hole in the hill. When the boys had been sworn to secrecy, they were allowed to crawl on their hands and knees into the hole. After two hundred yards the cave opened up. Sam lighted candle stubs, and led the way, ducking among passages, to a narrow opening in the wall. There was "a kind of room, all damp and sweaty and cold," and this was where Sam's gang held their meetings.

The real cave where Sam Clemens and Tom Blankenship played is like the cave described in *Tom Sawyer,* where Tom and Becky got lost. You can visit this cavern near Hannibal today.

The boy Sam Clemens did not spend all his time seeking adventures with his gang, however. Often he would wander off by himself along the river. He would lie dreaming for hours on some hilltop overlooking the Mississippi—his river—and watch the steamboats pass. And then he would change his mind about being a pirate. When he grew up, he decided, he would be a steamboat pilot instead, high up above the deck in a glorious glass cage—a lordly creature, whom everyone in the world had to obey.

Sam did become a river pilot when he grew up, and a very good pilot, too. For several years he led a happy, hard-working life, taking steamboats up and down the Mississippi River. That is how he came to choose the pen name by which the world knew him so well in later years. As a young man, when he began to write, he adopted a name taken from a river term—"Mark Twain." The term means two fathoms of water, that is, water about twelve feet deep—a welcome word to any pilot. For if the depth of the river is two fathoms, the steamboat can make a safe passage and the pilot knows that all is well. It is as Mark Twain that he was known in later years, when he became one of America's best-beloved authors, probably the most famous American of his day.

Rosa Bonheur Breaks Her Needle

By Mary Newlin Roberts

ROSA said good-by to her father in a low, disappointed voice. Her sewing bag hung limply in her hands.

"What is the trouble, Rosalie?"

Monsieur Bonheur turned at the doorway of the big studio and, setting down his box of paints, came back to her.

"I would like to go to the gallery with you, Papa," she said. "Maybe if I had been born a boy you would not make me study this dreadful dressmaking, and would help me more with my painting."

Her father put a hand on each of her shoulders and gave her a little shake.

"It's a hard life to be a painter even for a man, dearest girl. Sewing is far better for you. You have been such a wild little romp, it is good for you to be quiet and to try to grow into a useful and dignified woman. All my friends think it wise that you are learning dressmaking."

Monsieur Bonheur paused, as if he were not quite so sure as his friends about the matter. Then he hurried on, "Yes, yes, the life of an artist is full of hardship. Forget about it, Rosalie."

Rosa snatched a little green felt hat from a hook on the wall and pulled it down hard over her short curls.

"Will the squirrel be safe here all alone?" She was close to tears and wanted to change the subject. "And poor Bill the goat will bleat," she added lamely.

Her father clapped her on the back as if she were a boy. "Your goat will bleat whether we are near or not. He likes to listen to himself. And the squirrel is safe enough, though he nearly killed your poor father the other day by biting through the cord of a picture and letting it fall nearly on my head. Come now, put on your coat and we will start out together and tell each other all about everything tonight. You will sew your very best for my sake."

"I'll try," said Rosa, with a sinking heart.

They went out together and separated in the street. Monsieur Bonheur, who was an artist, went towards the Louvre, the greatest art gallery of Paris, and his daughter toward her dressmaking lessons. To sew all day, when her father would be at work in the midst of the glory of all those beautiful paintings, was a hard thought to endure. But she hurried on, with her chin set and her black eyes snapping. She loved her father dearly, and she was determined to please him.

Madame Gernstorf, the dressmaker, greeted her kindly, and set her to work upon a piece of silk. The sound of a turning wheel in the distance came from the workshop of Madame Gernstorf's husband. He was a maker of shell caps for guns, and Rosa, trying to settle to her sewing, would have preferred to turn the wheel and look at the shooting pieces.

"Do you think a painter's life is a hard one, and do you like the galleries?" she said suddenly.

"Why, I don't know," answered her teacher in a pinched voice because of the pins between her lips. She was finishing a ruffle on a dress that covered a headless dummy.

"You know," said Rosa, looking up and breaking her thread, which had become hopelessly tangled, "that figure is like some silly women—all dress and no brains on top."

Madame Gernstorf took out the pins and laughed.

"You are a sharp little lady sometimes, Rosa," she said. "Why do you talk of painting, when there are so many pretty dresses in the world? To be well dressed is a good thing. It is nice for a woman to look pretty, whether she has brains or not."

"I like to be comfortable in my clothes," said Rosa, "and I talk about painting because it interests me much more than dressmaking. But I mean to try to sew very well today all the same."

ROSA BONHEUR BREAKS HER NEEDLE

"You are putting that sleeve in upside down," cried the dressmaker. "Now let me show you again."

Rosa bit her lip and set to work with new determination. She thought the morning would never end. Every stitch she took had to be pulled out and done over again. At lunchtime she wished to eat her sandwiches where Monsieur Gernstorf was at work. Instead she sat demurely in her chair, setting her spools and needles to rights, and trying to forget her father painting in the great gallery of the Louvre among the pictures that she loved. After lunch, she fell to work with her needle, driving it in and out with fierce energy, but the harder she tried, the worse everything went.

Madame Gernstorf shook her head. "Oh, la la la!" she said, which is really French for, "Oh dear me!" "I sometimes wonder, Rosa Bonheur, if you will ever become a dressmaker."

Rosa flushed to her hair, and two hot tears rolled down her cheeks. At the same time she broke her needle with a snap. It

pricked her finger, but the pain of the prick was nothing to the pain of her bad work. She crumpled the silk dress into a miserable heap and sprang to her feet!

"Let me go home," she said. "Please let me go home, Madame! I cannot sew another stitch today or any day."

Madame Gernstorf brought her the small felt hat and coat, and helped her into them. She looked sad and clucked her tongue.

"Oh, la la la!" she said again and again, but she kissed Rosa good-by. "I wish you had been born a boy, *chérie*," she sighed.

Rosa ran almost all the way home, and rushed into the studio. Shutting the door behind her, she stood with her back to it. Her tears had dried, but she held her underlip tight with her teeth, for she was sharply disappointed over her failure.

"The whole trouble is, I am not meant to be a dressmaker," she said. "I can not help it even if Papa is angry."

The squirrel chattered a nervous greeting to her from a shelf, and the canary in a cage by the window burst into song. The old studio room looked dear and comforting with its easels and canvases—a different world from dresses and hems and ruffles. Rosa flung off her hat and threw her sewing bag down.

"So," she said, "it can't be helped. And now . . ."

She put on a large painting coat of her father's, rolling up the sleeves. Out of a closet she took a small canvas, a few of his discarded brushes and paints, and a bowl of dull copper which was filled with scarlet cherries and green leaves. She set them in a corner where the light struck them softly, and the shadows fell back of them in a most attractive manner. She put her little canvas on a chair, and seated herself on a low stool. On the canvas was her half-finished sketch, and Rosa's black eyes sparkled as she saw that it already had something of the beauty and light and shadow of the real fruit. She took an old palette and, squeezing out the remnants of paint left in the dried tubes, she set to work. Her father's big coat was shoved up over her knees, and her hair was pushed far back. She looked like a happy, eager boy, instead of a girl who had failed to become a dressmaker.

It was beginning to get dark when Rosa heard Monsieur Bonheur's step. She rose and took a hasty look at what she had done. Then she drew from a drawer three other sketches, and lined them up in full view. One of them was a likeness of her squirrel. Another showed the goat bleating and pulling on his rope. The third was a picture of a great, dignified bull she had seen being led through a side street of Paris.

She started to jerk off her father's painting coat, but it was too late. So she shrugged her small square shoulders and came to meet him, a little anxious, but too happy after her hour of painting to hide her excitement.

Monsieur Bonheur stopped short and stared at his daughter.

"Papa," said Rosa, talking fast, "you will have to forgive me. I fear, and so does Madame, that I will never learn to sew. I tried very hard for your sake, but I only broke my needle and pricked my finger and ruined the silk."

Her father's face grew long.

"And what are you doing here," he asked, "in my coat and all?"

"I am painting, Papa," Rosa hurried on. "You know, I watch

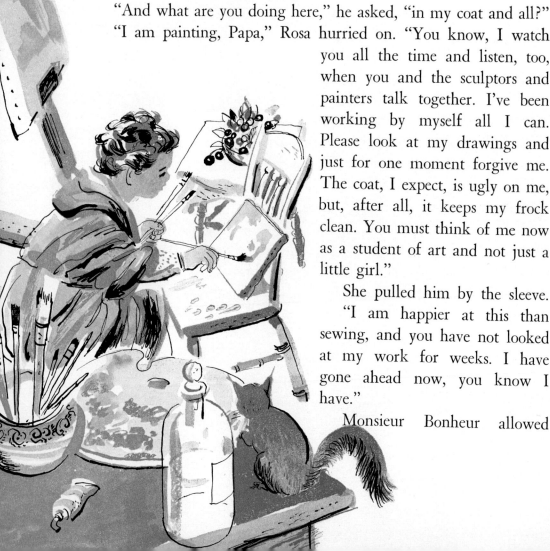

you all the time and listen, too, when you and the sculptors and painters talk together. I've been working by myself all I can. Please look at my drawings and just for one moment forgive me. The coat, I expect, is ugly on me, but, after all, it keeps my frock clean. You must think of me now as a student of art and not just a little girl."

She pulled him by the sleeve.

"I am happier at this than sewing, and you have not looked at my work for weeks. I have gone ahead now, you know I have."

Monsieur Bonheur allowed

himself to be pulled over in front of the small exhibition. He was frowning and stroking his beard.

"Rosalie," he said, shaking his head and jerking his shoulders, "What do you want to do? Do you seriously want to be a painter?"

"I do," said Rosa, holding up the tails of her coat and looking at her father with piercing eyes.

Monsieur Bonheur took up one sketch after another, the bull, and the squirrel, and the goat. He looked at the goat especially long. Then he turned the painting of the cherries to get a better light.

"What do you think? Tell me quickly, Papa," said Rosa, hopping on one foot with impatience.

"I think they are very good indeed," he said, reluctantly.

"So then," said his daughter dropping the long coat tails and placing her hands on her hips, "tomorrow you will take me with you to the Gallery and let me work and study and learn beside you?"

"Everyone, all my friends, will think me quite mad to let you do so, Rosalie."

"What of that? They can't know about what is best for you and me."

"People will stare at so young a girl in the Louvre, Rosa."

"I have thought of that," she said. "I have an idea to keep them from noticing a girl. Only take me and give me new brushes and good paints and an easel, and leave the rest to me."

ROSA BONHEUR BREAKS HER NEEDLE

Rosa's eyes were fairly burning with pleasure, and her square chin was set in a line of strength not to be mistaken.

Monsieur Bonheur drew her to him. "If in after years you regret this, Rosalie, if you find it hard to be a painter, if you wish ever that you had been only a happy simple woman with all that means, remember I tried to hold you back."

Rosa stood thoughtful for a moment and then she looked up into her father's face. "Thank you," she said. "But I think it will always be better this way. You will help me most by teaching me all you can. I will be ready early tomorrow."

She kissed him suddenly and ran to the squirrel, catching him and holding him close till the little creature grew quiet and content.

After that, day after day, two figures walked up the steps of the great gallery of the Louvre and through its long, richly-hung corridors. Two earnest figures, one big and one little. One was a man in a long painting coat. The other appeared to be a boy, dressed in a queer little quaint jacket and full trousers. At lunchtime they were to be seen eating together in the courtyard and drinking water from the pump. People called the small figure, "the Little Hussar" (soldier), because of her funny clothes, but they gathered none the less to watch her paint.

All day long and every day, Rosa worked, studying and copying and learning to her heart's content. Her father, watching, was glad that he had let her come. On Sundays he took her to the country to paint out-of-doors, and to make studies of animals; and her skill and power grew through the years.

From *Stories of the Youth of Artists*

Joyce Ballantyne

George Washington Carver, the Boy Who Had to Know

By M. I. Ross

A BIG MAN was walking on a path through the woods of his Missouri plantation, when he heard a slight noise behind some bushes. He took a step toward them, expecting to see a porcupine or deer; then he stood still in surprise. On the other side of the bushes he saw a small Negro boy kneeling between two beautiful specimens of tiger lilies.

"Why, George! What in the world are you doing here?"

The man was Moses Carver, owner of the cotton plantation, and the boy was their own young George Washington Carver. He had been born a slave during the War between the States. When he was only a few weeks old, the Carver slaves had been stolen by raiders. By the time they were overtaken, the mother had been sold again. But Mr. Carver had been able to get the baby back by trading a broken-down race horse for him.

The Carvers had grown very fond of the little boy with the dark, intelligent eyes, and they named him George Washington

103

because he tried so hard to be truthful. They had also given him their own family name, as that was the custom with the slaves.

But now, in 1872, the war had been over for several years. George Washington Carver was free, but at eight he was frail and small for his age, and looked not much bigger than a porcupine as he knelt among the flowers.

"This is my garden," he explained proudly as he pointed out the different plants. He had collected a remarkable botanical garden of Missouri specimens. Some were new to Mr. Carver, many very rare, but all were thriving under George's care. There was a neat strong fence of sticks to keep out animals.

Mr. Carver was astonished. "So this is where you go when you scoot out of the house at four o'clock every morning!"

George nodded shyly. He seemed to know by instinct what to do for ailing plants, how to protect them from disease and insects. He asked Mr. Carver the names of some of the flowers.

Mr. Carver laughed. "I only know the names of the common ones. I've never even seen some of these."

George tipped up a big healthy bud on one of the stalks. "Nobody seems to know what this one is, but it's going to have a nice flower. I wish I knew its name."

CARVER

Mr. Carver shook his head. "It's beyond me, George. I'm afraid you'll have to wait until you can read. Then you can hunt for the names in botany books."

They started home together.

"When will that be?" George asked.

"When will what be?"

"Till I can read botany books."

Mr. Carver was thoughtful. It was too bad that such a bright boy could not be educated. But the schools near them were only for white children. The Carvers, like many other plantation owners, had been almost ruined by the war, and they had no money to send George away to school.

"I'll hunt around the house and see if I can find an old blue-

backed speller we used to have. That might give you a start."

Mr. Carver told everybody about George's remarkable garden. It was not long before his skill with plants was well known, and people began to call him "the plant doctor."

In the meantime, George had held Mr. Carver to his promise. The blue-backed speller was found.

"You see, the words are all spelled with letters, and the letters are called the alphabet." Mr. Carver was no teacher, but George got the idea at once. It seemed no time at all before he had gone through the whole speller and knew all the words. The Carvers asked each other, "What are we going to do with him now?"

"Give him the Bible to read," Mrs. Carver suggested.

Young George read for a long time in the Bible. But after awhile he grew restless to learn more. The Carvers were very sorry that they could not help him. George understood. He began asking questions of the more traveled people in the neighborhood. One day he came running home with very exciting news. "There is a school in Neosho, only eight miles away."

"But you can't walk sixteen miles a day."

"I could go there and live."

The Carvers hated to explain again that they could not afford to help him.

"But I don't need help!"

"Where would you live? What would you live on? You had better stay here till you're old enough to earn a living."

"Old enough!" George laughed. "I'm ten! That's plenty old enough."

There was no holding George back, and at last Mr. and Mrs. Carver gave up. One day they stood on their steps, watching their small namesake trudge off down the road toward Neosho. He grew smaller and smaller, till he reached the bend in the road. There he turned and waved reassuringly to them.

"He is so little," Mrs. Carver said.

"Don't worry. He'll be back," her husband answered. "He'll have to find out for himself how hard it is."

Moses Carver was wrong. It was a long time before they saw George again. When the boy arrived at Neosho he looked first to see if the school really was there. It was—a one-room log cabin school with log benches and one teacher. He was so delighted that he forgot he had no place to sleep.

That thought soon occurred to him, however. The walk had made him very hungry, and he had no money. Well, he could chop wood, he decided. He had been taking entire charge of the Carvers' fires and wood toting. He could carry water and wash dishes. He could even cook. Mrs. Carver had taught him.

He managed to earn a few pennies for food. He found an old horse barn where he slept for several nights. Then in the round of asking for work he came to Mr. Watkins.

"Why do you want to work in Neosho?" Mr. Watkins asked.

"To go to school, sir."

"To go to school!" This was very unusual for a Negro boy then.

Mr. Watkins took George home. Mrs. Watkins was just as pleased by his eager longing to learn and his gentle manners as her husband had been.

"Indeed," Dr. Carver said in later years, "Mr. and Mrs. Watkins allowed me to stay in their home in exchange for the work I could do. They treated me as if I were a member of their family."

Their kindness was not needed for long. In one year George had learned everything he could from the teacher in the little school. This teacher had not had the advantages of higher learning, but was in sympathy with George's ambitions. He helped him to find a high school sixty miles farther off in Fort Scott, Kansas, and George went there when the year was up.

It was still remarkable for an eleven-year-old boy to be so hungry for learning that he would hunt out a school in a strange town and go there with no means of support but his own hands. But he had done it at ten, why not at eleven? He spent six years in Fort Scott, and graduated from the high school when he was seventeen.

In addition, he had been able to save enough doing odd jobs to start a business of his own, a laundry. He was still small for his age. Most of his white customers would have been surprised to learn that the little delivery boy, who brought back their sheets

so snowy white, was also the washing machine and the ironer.

From his laundry business, George Washington Carver saved enough to pay his train fare to a college town in Iowa. His school record was so high that the college had accepted his application by mail. But when he appeared and they saw that he was a Negro, they refused to admit him.

George was disappointed but not bitter. He decided that this feeling against his race was just one of the problems that he had to solve. Since he had no money with which to leave town, he cheerfully set up his laundry again.

In time he made his way to Simpson's College and then to Iowa State College at Ames. There he received his degrees and became one of the teachers. Then Booker T. Washington, famous Negro founder of Tuskegee Institute in Alabama, took him to Tuskegee to organize and head their agricultural department and experiment station.

Later George Washington Carver earned the name "Savior of the South" by his many wonderful achievements in the field of agricultural chemistry. When the boll weevil killed the cotton crop on which most Southern farmers depended to earn their livings, he persuaded them to plant peanuts. Single-handed, he invented three hundred products using the chemicals that make up peanuts. He also thought of many uses for sweet potatoes and pecans, and he invented a line of paints that could be made from Alabama clays at almost no cost. Many farmers who had been desperately poor were made more prosperous and comfortable because of what he had done.

Leaders in far-off India and the Soviet Union, as well as the industrial leaders in his own country, sought Dr. Carver's help as a research chemist. Many men who knew him well said he might just as easily have been a great musician or artist. One of his paintings was requested by the famous European art gallery at Luxemburg. Another was exhibited in the Chicago World's Fair and valued at $4,000. All have been painted with colors he had taken from Alabama clays, and some on canvas he made himself from cornstalk fibers.

But perhaps his most remarkable achievement was to put himself through the entire elementary school in a single year at the age of ten. If he had had parents to encourage him, or if there had been friends in Neosho to help him, it would be easier to understand. His life might be compared to one of the flowers that he loved. In its seeds the flower contained all the elements to make it grow.

The Map That Came to Life

A Story of Robert Louis Stevenson

By Elizabeth Rider Montgomery

ANYONE who hasn't read *Treasure Island* has missed one of the best adventure stories ever written. Buried treasure, pirates, ships, castaways—*Treasure Island* has all those, and more thrills besides. It's a story for boys—for strong, healthy boys who like plenty of action. But it was written by a man who had been weak and sickly all his life, who had never been able to romp and play like other boys. And it was written because a map began to swarm with people in that man's imagination.

Robert Louis Stevenson had returned to his home in Scotland in 1880 after a long stay in America. He brought back with him his new wife and her young son, Lloyd.

But the climate of Scotland was too harsh for the man who had been an invalid all his life. Doctors ordered him to a health resort in Switzerland.

Though he did not like Switzerland as well as his native Scotland, Stevenson did not complain. In spite of homesickness and ill health, he found plenty to do to keep busy and happy. For one thing, there was his writing. Already the author of several successful books, he wrote whenever he felt well enough, always trying to write something better than he had done before.

And then there was Lloyd, his stepson. Stevenson and the boy had grown to be great friends. They played elaborate war games together, using tin soldiers and a huge map on the floor. They made pictures and block prints together, and operated a hand printing set. Yes, Stevenson and his stepson were great pals.

One day Lloyd said to his stepfather, "I wish you'd write a good story for me."

Stevenson looked at the boy affectionately. "A good story? What kind of a story is that, Lloyd?"

"Oh, you know," answered the boy. "Lots of excitement. Pirates, maybe. Fights. And *no women.*

"No women?" asked Stevenson. "Why not?"

"Oh, women spoil a good story. They are always afraid a fellow is going to get hurt."

"All right, Lloyd," laughed Stevenson. "I'll write a good story for you one of these days—with no women in it."

It was many days later, however, that Robert Louis Stevenson got an idea for the "good story." The man and the boy were sitting on the floor drawing pictures. Stevenson was coloring a map he had made—a beautiful, elaborate map of an imaginary island.

"Look here!" he exclaimed to Lloyd. "Look at the island on this map. Wouldn't it be a wonderful place for buried treasure?"

Lloyd crawled over to see, and the dog, Woggs, followed him.

"Oh, yes!" cried the boy. "That's a fine island for buried treasure. But how did the treasure get there, do you suppose?"

"Pirates," said Stevenson solemnly. "Pirates put it there, and pirates are trying to take it away. Can't you see a one-eyed pirate behind that rock?"

Mrs. Stevenson had come into the room while her husband was talking, but the man and the boy were so busy studying the map that neither of them heard her. Only the dog looked up, and

wagged his tail.

"Oh, Louis!" exclaimed Mrs. Stevenson fondly. "What a boy you are! Seeing people on a map where there is nothing but harbors and mountains."

Stevenson looked up at his wife and scrambled to his feet.

"Fanny," he said earnestly, "I can see a whole swarm of people on that island. Pirates, castaways, buccaneers—and a boy: a fine, strong, steady boy like Lloyd here. And I'm going to write a good story about them."

"You are?" cried Lloyd. "Oh, that's great! Read it to me as you write it, won't you?"

And so Stevenson began the writing of *Treasure Island,* though at first he called the story of the map that came to life, *The Sea Cook.*

Each evening he read to his family what he had written during the day. And to his surprise not only his stepson listened raptly, but his wife and his father as well. In fact, the old man was as enthusiastic as was the boy.

And when it was finished (with no women, as Lloyd had ordered, except for Jim's mother, who is necessary at the very beginning) and was published, Stevenson found that he had written a story that was loved by boys of all ages, from nine to ninety.

From *The Story Behind Great Books*

The Wright Brothers Learn to Fly

By Joseph Cottler and Haym Jaffe

FROM the time when Wilbur Wright was eleven years old and his brother Orville was seven, they had shown an interest in flying. It began in this way. Their father, Bishop Milton Wright, once walked into the room where they were playing. His hand concealed something.

"Here's something for you," he said, and into the air he tossed a whirring object.

"It flies," cried the boys, as they watched it spin across the room and strike the ceiling. There it fluttered about for a few moments before it fell. The boys jumped for the toy, and eagerly examined it.

"What is it?" asked Orville.

"A toy bat," suggested Wilbur.

"It's a helicopter," explained their father.

"How does it work?" they asked.

Bishop Wright showed them that the "bat" was only a cork and bamboo frame, covered with paper; that it rose in the air by

means of some twisted rubber bands.

"Where did you get it, Father?" asked Wilbur.

"I bought it when I was in New York. Not long ago there lived a certain Frenchman, who fell sick and became a cripple. Since the poor fellow could not walk, he began to dream of flying. That is how he came to invent this flying toy. Once he tried to make a real flying machine, but he failed. Finally everyone laughed at his ambitions, and he died of a broken heart."

The boys were silent for a moment. Then one exclaimed, "Perhaps some day a great man will succeed."

"Perhaps," replied their father.

Again and again they flew the toy. "I wonder if we can make it fly higher," said Wilbur.

"Let's make a bigger 'bat'," replied his brother. They did make another flying toy, somewhat larger, but this one did not fly as well as the one which their father had brought them.

"Perhaps we did not make our 'bat' right," they said. "We must try again." What puzzled them was that the larger the toy, the less time would it stay up in the air. And, beyond a certain size, their "bat" would not fly at all.

Defeated, they turned their interest to kites, which would stay

THE WRIGHT BROTHERS LEARN TO FLY

up in the air. But the helicopter always remained a vivid memory to the Wright brothers.

When the boys grew older, they turned to the craze of the day, bicycles. They set up a little shop for repairing and making wheels. They made their own tools, even such complicated ones as lathes.

Before long people began to know and like these quiet, pleasant brothers. Not only were their wheels well-made, but on them they installed a splendid safety brake which they had invented.

One day they thought of having a bit of fun. They rode all over town on a huge tandem bicycle they built. It was made of two old high wheels, connected by a long gas pipe. "It's a better sight than seeing a circus," was the town's comment.

Later the lure of flying seized them. They became deeply interested in the experiments which Otto Lilienthal, a German engineer, was making with flying machines. One day they read about the accident which had resulted in his death, and they sent for a copy

of the book which he had written about flying. They liked the way he had emphasized the idea of constant practice.

"Every bird is an acrobat," he wrote. "Whoever would master the air must learn to imitate the birds. We must fly and fall, and fall and fly, until we can fly without falling."

From then on the brothers thought less and less of their bicycle business. They read all they could about flying, and they began to watch the birds on the wing. If, when they were in their shop, one of the brothers spied a flock of birds flying by, "Birds!" he would shout. Both would drop their work and rush to the window, gazing until the birds were out of sight.

For the rest of the day, during their spare time, they would argue about what they had seen—about how the bird soars, how its wings are shaped when outstretched, how it balances. For days on end they talked about these matters.

"I'm right," Orville would say. "It's like this . . ."

"No, I'm right," Wilbur would insist. "It's like that . . ."

"Well," Orville would hesitate, "I guess you are right."

Wilbur would be silent for some moments. "No, Orville, I see that you have the better idea," he would finally admit. And they would laugh and go on happily.

They could hardly wait till Sunday afternoon. Then, for hours and hours, they would lie on their backs on a hill outside of Dayton, watching buzzards soar on the rising current of air.

For five years they studied and argued about flying. They made tiny machines which they flew in the air like kites.

"I've figured it out," reflected one of the brothers. "Lilienthal, in five years, spent about five hours of actual gliding in the air. If we could only find some way by which we could practice by the hour instead of by the second, we could solve the problem. . . ."

To this most dangerous of hobbies, they began to devote all their time and energy. After much study, they decided that if they could lie flat in the airplane instead of standing upright, as in Lilienthal's machine, the wind resistance could be reduced. And instead of the rider's shifting in the machine to balance himself and steer the airplane in the direction he wanted to fly, they decided that the machine should do the work. They put a rudder in front, and soon were able to control the airplane.

One day an elderly man appeared on the field where they were practicing in the gliding machine which they had made. He watched them leap and soar, grasshopper fashion, from spot to spot on their wings of wood and canvas.

"Do you young men know," he said, "that you have come nearer to the art of flying than any other man who ever lived?"

It was Octave Chanute speaking. He, too, had been experimenting with flying machines, and he knew more about the history of flying than any man in America. He was most encouraging, and the brothers worked harder than ever. Finally they built a flying machine with an engine. They had to make the engine themselves, because no company would make one for them. Then they took their machine to Kitty Hawk, North Carolina, to try it out.

On December 17, 1903, they were ready. A general invitation was sent to the people of the town to come and watch the fliers. Only five people were willing to face the cold December wind.

The machine was made ready. The engine was started. Orville Wright got in.

And then a miracle! The airplane rose and stayed in the air twelve seconds! For the first time in history, a machine carrying a man raised itself into the air by its own power and landed without being wrecked.

Twelve seconds! From such beginnings, we have seen man fly across the oceans and around the earth. At last man has nothing for which to envy the birds. He can fly faster than any living bird.

Adapted from *Heroes of Civilization*

Thomas Alva Edison, Young Scientist

By Winifred E. Wise

THOMAS ALVA EDISON was much too busy to go coasting, skating, or fishing often, or to join the rest of the gang in snowball fights. "Al," as he was called as a boy, had just found a scientific book he could understand, and he was completely absorbed in it. He read with breathless curiosity about the thousands of things he wished to know: why vehicles have wheels, why boats float, how lightning rods work, and so on. This book was his key to the wonderland of science. Eager to try the hundreds of experiments described in the book, he bought some equipment with his limited pocket money and set up a laboratory in his home basement.

Here Al did a number of experiments. From the first he kept records of these, writing data and making sketches on loose pieces of paper which he preserved in scrapbooks. But after awhile he began to grow restless. He was tired of being a baby who had to ask his father or mother for pocket money. The money he got looked small when it came to buying batteries and Leyden jars for

THOMAS ALVA EDISON

his experiments, or delicate scales which would measure a six-teenth of an ounce. Besides, he was curious about the stirring world outside his quiet home town. What could a twelve-year-old boy do about it?

One day he was down at the depot in Port Huron, Michigan, where he lived. Standing next to several train officials, he over-heard them say that a boy was needed to sell newspapers and candy on the train between Fort Gratiot and Detroit. Here was his chance! If he could get the job, he could earn money to buy the equipment he needed, and he could travel to the wonderful city of Detroit every day.

Plucking up his courage, Al Edison turned to the men and said, "I heard you talking about wanting a train boy. How would I do?"

Because he looked as bright as a five-dollar gold piece, he was hired immediately. When he went home and told his mother that he had a job, she said, "I'll talk to your father about it."

That night there was a family conference in the Edison home. Both parents thought that the hours on the train would be too

JANICE HOLLAND

long, and both were afraid to let their son go alone to the big city of Detroit. But it was not unusual, in those days, for a boy of twelve to strike out on his own. The Edisons knew that Al would have to start earning his own living soon—perhaps he might as well begin at once. It was not as though he would be going away from home for good. Every night he could come home to sleep under his own roof. Every morning his mother could see that his ears were washed, that his stomach was full of good food, and that stray buttons on his coat and pants were sewed on. Mr. and Mrs. Edison finally agreed to allow him to take the job.

Al's train left Fort Gratiot at seven in the morning and reached Detroit at ten. Returning, it left Detroit at half-past six in the evening and arrived at Fort Gratiot at half-past nine. Loudly the new train boy peddled his stock-in-trade through the smoker and the "ladies' car," calling out, "Big double-roasted, double-jointed peanuts, ham sandwiches, popcorn." The passengers had to eat his wares for breakfast, because trains did not then have diners. Then he came back, laden with reading matter, and tossed a dime novel or a recent newspaper or magazine into the lap of each traveler. In a few minutes, he re-appeared to collect either the publications or the money for them. He usually collected the money, because nearly everyone bought a newspaper and a magazine.

One day he saw a sign, "Detroit Free Library," and hurried into the low brick building. Looking at the rows and rows of books, he thought to himself, "Why not read all the books here? Then I will know almost everything in the world."

He measured off the shelves and decided that he ought to be able to read about a foot of books a week. This he set out to do, reading yards of histories, geographies, novels, and scientific works to satisfy his eager curiosity. But the more books he read, the more books there were to read, as the library went on buying books. He might as well have tried to bail out the sea with a thimble. Soon he settled down to reading mostly scientific books, with a poem or novel when his studies got too heavy. His favorites were Longfellow's *Evangeline* and the novels of Victor Hugo.

Before long Al was very much at home in Detroit. By the time the conductor on the early evening Port Huron train called, "All aboard!" young Edison was all aboard too, arms full of newly bought chemicals for his experiments. Before the train was out of the yards, he was walking through the aisles, peddling his papers and candies. When the train stopped at a station, he got off to sell newspapers to his regular customers in the town. From the start he earned at least forty dollars a month. After giving his mother a dollar every day, he spent all the rest on chemicals and laboratory equipment.

He had gone to work chiefly in order to get money to buy materials for his experiments. Before, he had had the time for experimenting, but no money. Now he had the money, but no time. The only solution was a "laboratory on wheels."

The baggage car on the train was divided into three compartments—one for mail, one for packages and trunks, and the third for smoking. Being stuffy, the smoking section was not used for its original purpose, but was turned over to the train boy. Here Al kept his newspapers, candy, and other stock-in-trade, and here he proposed to set up his laboratory. With the conductor's permission, he moved the chemicals, test tubes, and bottles from his basement sanctum to the train. After that he spent the tag-ends of his time on both runs of the train doing delicate chemical experiments.

But that fall Old Man Bad Luck came knocking at Al's door. One night he had so many newspaper customers in the town of Fraser that he did not hear the conductor shout, "All aboard!" The train started off; and Al ran after it, caught the handrail beside the steps of the last car, and hung there. The train picked up speed

and dragged him over the gravel roadbed at a fast clip. Out of
breath from running, and with hands stiff with cold, he could not
pull himself onto the platform of the train. A brakeman grabbed
him by the scruff of the neck and tried to pull him up. His grip
slipped; so he caught the boy's ears as convenient handles and
yanked him to safety. Al felt something in his ears snap, and from
that moment he began to grow deaf.

Al's fortunes hit further rough going a few weeks later when
the springless cars hit a bit of rough track. As the train rattled over
the poorly laid rails, a stick of phosphorus was shaken from a
water jar in his laboratory, and set fire to the baggage car. When
the conductor arrived on the scene, Al was trying to fan out the
flames with his coat. Shoving him aside, the conductor soon
smothered the blaze with buckets of sand and water. Although the
fire had done little damage, he was so enraged over this accident
that he dumped the young scientist off at the next station, and,

THOMAS ALVA EDISON

with him, his laboratory equipment. This done, the train puffed away into the late fall twilight, and Al's career as a train boy ended.

Within a few days, however, he was busy setting up test tubes in his home basement and optimistically planning future experiments. He had almost forgotten his unpleasant last afternoon on the train. Never one to worry over accidents after they happened, he later said, "Spilt milk doesn't interest me. I have spilt lots of it. While I have always felt it for a few days, it is quickly forgotten, and I turn again to the future."

Meanwhile Thomas Alva Edison, now fif-teen, had been learning telegraphy. He became a telegraph operator in various cities of the United States and Canada—positions which gave him spare time to carry on his experiments. At the age of twenty-two, he sold his first successful invention, a stock ticker, for forty thousand dollars. With this money he opened his first laboratory. During his long, eventful life, he took out patents on more than one thousand inventions. He helped to give us the phonograph, the incandescent electric light, electric railroads, motion pictures, and many, many other things which have changed our way of living.

Adapted from *Thomas Alva Edison, the Youth and His Times*

Janice Holland

Teddy Roosevelt, the Boy Naturalist

By Ruth Cromer Weir

YOUNG Teddy Roosevelt liked to read about great men and he decided that he would be a great man, too, some day. He especially liked to read stories about explorers. He liked to study insects and snakes and fishes and birds and wild animals. So he planned to be a great naturalist.

Once when his younger sister, Connie, was away from home on a visit, "Teddy" wrote her about his latest pets. "I have got four white mice," the letter said, "white-skinned, red-eyed velvety creatures, very tame, for I let them run all over me."

One day Teddy put a family of white mice in the refrigerator to keep them safely. Although Teddy's mother was kind, keeping mice in the refrigerator was too much even for a loving mother. Mrs. Roosevelt disposed of them. But when Teddy found that his mice were gone, he could hardly bear it. "It's the loss to science! The loss to science!" he stormed.

Teddy's mother often sent him to a store on Broadway, near his home in New York City, to buy strawberries. There one day Teddy saw a dead seal that the fishermen had killed in the harbor. Young Teddy thought that this was surely the most wonderful "specimen" that any naturalist could wish to study. Teddy asked the storekeeper for permission to measure it. Then he set to work on the most important scientific study he had ever made. He had no tape measure, but quickly slid a folding ruler from a bulging pocket. With great care, the boy measured the dead seal. Around the body he placed the ruler. Then he carefully measured the animal from the end of the nose to the tip of the tail flipper. Before he left the store, young Roosevelt bought a new notebook, in which he drew a picture of the seal. He wrote a complete description of the animal and listed all its measurements. In the days that followed, Teddy visited the store time and again. At last, when the store-keeper disposed of the seal's body, he gave the skull to Teddy.

How proudly Teddy walked home with that skull! His cousins, Johnnie and Jimmie Roosevelt, who lived in the house next door, were almost as interested in it as Teddy. Suddenly Teddy had one of his bright ideas. "Let's have a museum," he suggested. "This can be our first scientific specimen."

It was decided that the museum should be named the "Roosevelt Museum of Natural History."

After that, the Roosevelt home became a livelier place than ever. Snakes and lizards slid from dresser drawers. Field mice scurried from closets, ground squirrels scampered across the floor, and frogs and toads hopped from under Teddy's bed. There were other animals, too, some partly preserved for the new museum.

One bright day, Teddy was on his way home from a successful hunting trip with his cousin, Jimmie. They had found two toads of a strange, new kind, for the museum. The sacks which they had taken were already full of new specimens of insects. The boys' pockets were likewise full, so the two decided to carry the toads home under their hats. They were almost home when, rounding a corner, they found themselves face to face with Mrs. Hamilton Fish.

Mrs. Hamilton Fish was a friend of their parents, and was a very proper lady. Mrs. Fish smiled. "Good afternoon, boys," she said.

Teddy and Jimmie exchanged a quick glance. Polite boys could do only one thing. "Good afternoon," they replied sickly, as they tipped their hats.

TEDDY

Out jumped the two valued toad specimens, lost forever to science.

It was not long after that Teddy advertised for field mice to swell the museum. He offered thirty-five cents for each family of mice and ten cents for each mouse delivered to him. Then he left home for a visit in the country, forgetting all about the mice.

Soon a farmer appeared at the Roosevelt door with two families of mice. "Your brother advertised for these," the farmer explained.

Anna, Teddy's older sister, paid for Teddy's mice. But this was only the beginning. Men and boys and more men and more boys came to the Roosevelts' door with more mice, each in answer to Teddy's advertisement.

Anna proved to be a really wonderful sister. Mice were the last thing on earth that she wanted to buy. But she bought them all with her own money. What is more, she kept them fed until Teddy's return.

The Roosevelt boys had their museum in Teddy's room. They were always adding new insects, birds, animals, and reptiles to their collection. Before long, Teddy's room bulged and reeked with grubby specimens. At last, the maid could stand it no longer. She said she would quit working for the Roosevelts if something was not done about Teddy's room.

With the help of Teddy's father, the museum was moved to the third floor. Teddy's father also found a taxidermist to teach Teddy

ROOSEVELT

the scientific way to preserve and mount museum specimens.

Teddy had already started to write journals which he called his natural histories. In one, his *Natural History of Insects,* he wrote: "All the insects that I write about in this book inhabbit North America. Now and then a friend has told me something about them but mostly I have gained their habits from ofserv-a-tion."

Although Teddy mispelled many words, as he did "inhabit" and "observation," he almost always knew their meaning. Already he had learned some of the first lessons of a great naturalist. He knew how to make careful observations and how to keep a record of them. What is more, he could understand what he saw. Later, young Teddy Roosevelt carried out his plan to be a naturalist.

Theodore Roosevelt also became known as a great President of the United States. But it was, probably, his lifelong interest in nature that prepared him to make his greatest contribution to his country. For it was Theodore Roosevelt who helped to draw up the plan known as the Conservation of National Resources. This wonderful plan began the movement to save our forests, our winding rivers and streams, our bright wild birds, our wild animals, and our rich minerals. It has helped to keep America a productive as well as a beautiful land. The plan also set aside some of our most beautiful regions as national parks, where, every year, thousands of people enjoy many wonders of nature, and birds and animals are always safe.

The Story of Jane Addams

By Jean Brown Wagoner

LITTLE Jane Addams tiptoed to the window and pushed the shutter open a crack. Cold air rushed in on her bare feet. A light snow was falling. "Ooo-ooo! It's colder than ever." She was about to pop back into bed when she heard Father's voice. He was out on the front steps calling to someone.

"I won't be at the mill this morning," he was saying, "Jane and I are going to the city."

"Going to the city!" cried Jane, and fairly jumped into her clothes. The Addams family lived in the little town of Cedarville, Illinois, and a trip to the bigger town of Freeport was always an event to look forward to. Jane hurried down to breakfast but found that Father had already gone down to the barn to hitch up Prince.

"You're going in the new buggy," said Polly, the housekeeper who had taken care of Jane since her mother died. "In the new buggy! Oh my!" shouted Jane. She hadn't ridden in the new buggy, which Father had driven home just the week before. It was a beautiful glossy black trimmed with a narrow yellow stripe. Now Jane was going all the way to Freeport in this elegant carriage, and she was almost too excited to eat.

Father was at the door with the buggy before she had finished her chocolate. He lifted her onto the seat beside him, and tucked the covers around her. He set a box under her feet, for her legs were too short for her feet to touch the floor. Then he lifted the reins, and off they went, whirling out of the drive in a flurry of snow, through the streets of Cedarville, and down the road toward Freeport.

Jane loved Freeport. Everyone was so friendly. When they stopped at the inn, the stableboy ran out to hold the horse. The owner came out to welcome them. People on the street bowed and smiled.

While Father went to the bank, Jane went to William Walton's store. That was her favorite store, because Mr. Walton always saved samples of his finest cloth for her. He knew she used them for her dolls. Sometimes there were pieces from New York and London and Paris. He knew the names of some of the great ladies who wore dresses of these materials. He told her about the balls that were given for them.

Jane didn't have time to visit as long as usual today. "I have to stop at the old mill I used to own here," Father said, "so we'll have to start home early."

Mr. Walton wrapped up the beautiful bits of satin and silk for Jane. He helped her into the carriage as if she were one of the elegant ladies herself.

Father left the city by a different road this time. They didn't go down the wide street with the big shade trees and fine homes with lovely gardens and lawns. They went down the narrowest, dirtiest streets Jane had ever seen.

"Why, Father, these people haven't any yards at all. There isn't any room for the children to play. Why did the people build such little houses so close together?"

"They haven't enough money to buy bigger houses or yards," he answered. "They have to live where they can walk to work, too."

Jane stared at the ugly houses and streets and the children who played in the dirt because there was no grass.

"When I grow up, Father, I shall have a big house, a great big house," she said decidedly. "But I won't have it where all the other big houses are. I'll have it right in the middle of these little houses. Then I'll let all the children come and play in my yard and my house."

The years went by, and almost before she knew it, Jane Addams was grown up. After she graduated from college she went abroad and lived in the big cities she had read about—London, Paris, Rome. She wasn't a plain little girl any longer. She was a beautiful young lady dressed in velvets and silks, who went to the grand balls and to the opera. She visited the art galleries and museums and libraries throughout the world, and studied about the wonderful things

130

she saw. But there was one thing she saw that was not wonderful or beautiful or good. It was ugly.

Back of the grand hotels and behind the opera houses and the art galleries lived the poor people. The only homes they knew were dark, dirty little rooms in dark, dirty buildings. The streets they lived on were so narrow a man could stand in the middle and touch both sides. The sunlight never reached them.

"Where do the boys and girls play?" asked Jane. No one answered her. They thought this rich American girl was queer to ask such a question.

"Why won't someone do something to help them?" she begged.

Finally one man said angrily, "You think the poor here have a hard time. It is just as bad in your own country."

"In the United States," said Jane, "people would do something if someone told them and showed them that it was bad."

He laughed at her in scorn. "Well, who's going to tell them so that they will listen. You?"

"Yes, I will," said Jane to herself. She went to her hotel and began to pack her trunks. "I'm

131

going home. All the beauty in the world can't make me happy when I know there are people at my back door who are starving. The people of the United States are kind and generous. I'll go live with the poor in the big cities. Then I'll tell my friends about them. I know they will make things better."

So Jane Addams came back to America. People said, "Now Jane will live in a fine house and be a fashionable lady."

Jane said, "Now I am going to do what I planned to do when I was a little girl."

She went to Chicago. There, in the worst part of the city, she found a big house. It had once been a beautiful home in the center of a park, and had been built by a man named Hull. It was still called Hull House, but now it was part of the tenement district. Foreigners from all countries were crowded together there. There weren't any trees or grass or flowers within miles. Dirty, rickety buildings walled in filthy, muddy streets. The crying of children, the angry shouts of men, the shrill voices of tired mothers filled the air. Whole families lived in one room.

Jane Addams rented Hull House, and she and two good friends went to work. They scraped off layers of dirty paint and wallpaper. They scrubbed and polished. They brought their fine rugs and pictures and furniture. Outside was the ugly, smelly city. Inside was a clean, fine home, and Jane and her friends moved into it.

Then she began to get acquainted with her neighbors. She invited them to her house for tea. She used her best china and her finest silver. There were roses on the table and a fire in the fireplace. The room was so pretty the women felt embarrassed. But Jane was friendly and soon they were telling her about Italy, their native country. They told her how homesick they were sometimes. The next day they came again and brought their friends and their husbands. How they loved Jane's beautiful home and her pretty things! Most of all they loved her kind heart.

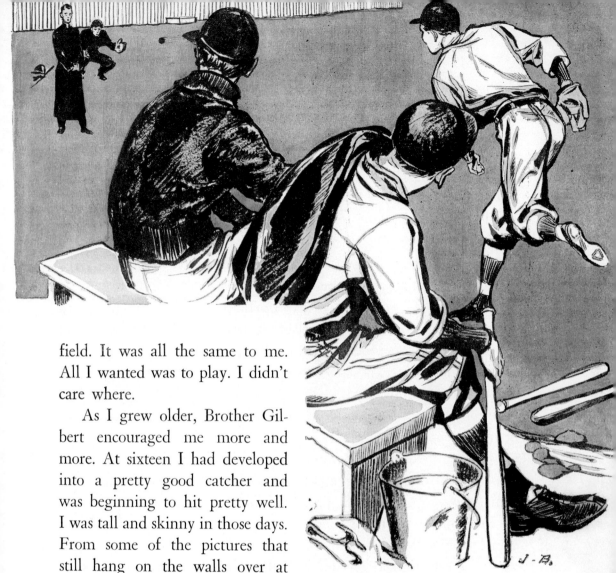

THE CHIEF AT WARM SPRINGS

One day Jane was watching some little children in the street. They were making mud pies; that is, they were trying to. But every few minutes they had to run out of the way of the horses and big wagons that came lumbering down the street.

"Why don't you keep your children at home?" Jane Addams asked the mothers of the neighborhood. "Aren't you afraid they'll be killed playing in the streets?"

"Some of them do get killed," replied the mothers. "But what can we do? We have to go to work from early morning till late at night. If we leave the children in the house, they play too near the stove and catch fire."

"I tie my little ones to the bed so that they can't get into mischief," said another, "but they cry because they get hungry."

"Let the smallest ones come to my house," said Jane. "I'll take care of them while you work."

THE STORY OF JANE ADDAMS

More and more women left their little ones for Jane to look after. She had a big sand pile built where they could make all the mud pies they wanted. She bought storybooks and read to them. Soon the older children begged to be allowed to play there, too. Jane took them all in. She bought tools and games and more books.

"I need more money and many helpers," she said. She went to her friends, rich and poor, and told them about her neighbors, and their needs.

Then just what Jane had told the man in Europe would happen did happen. The people of the United States began to do something when they heard about the poor people. The woman that owned Hull House gave it to Jane rent-free. Another woman gave money for a big nursery. A man who owned a block of tenement buildings gave them to her. "Fix them up, tear them down, do what you want," he said.

Young women and young men from good homes came and lived at Hull House and helped take care of Jane's neighbors. They looked after the little children, they scrubbed floors, washed windows, cooked for Jane's guests, planned parties and club meetings. They helped keep Hull House bright and clean.

"This still is not enough," said Jane Addams. "My neighbors have to work too long and don't make enough to live on. We must make laws that won't allow little children to work in factories. The working places of all people must be light and airy and safe. Working hours must be shorter so that men will have time to enjoy their families. Men must be paid more so that they can buy the things they need."

The people of the United States listened to Jane Addams. They made more just and kindly laws. All these wonderful things that she brought about took a good many years and a great deal of hard work. But she made her city a better place to live in.

Adapted from *Jane Addams, Little Lame Girl*

134

Babe Ruth's Own Story

By George Herman Ruth

MY earliest memories center about the dirty, traffic-crowded streets of Baltimore's river front.

Crowded streets they were too, noisy with the roar of heavy trucks whose drivers yelled and aimed blows with their driving whips at the legs of kids who made the streets their playground.

A rough, tough neighborhood, but I liked it. There in those crooked winding streets I staged my first fight, and lost, I think. There too I played my first baseball.

Many people thought I was an orphan. I wasn't. My folks lived in Baltimore and my father worked in the district where I was raised. We were poor. Very poor. There were times when we never knew where the next meal was coming from. But I never minded. I was no worse off than the other kids with whom I played and fought.

I don't know how I happened to be sent to St. Mary's school. It wasn't so much a school as it was a home where kids like me could be cared for and trained and taught as they should be. All I remember is that I was a loose-jointed, gangling, dirty-faced kid in knee pants playing in the street, where one day a round-faced pleasant little man in clerical garb came over to talk to me.

I thought he was a priest and I called him Father, and tipped my cap when I spoke to him.

"Not Father," he said, smiling, "Just Brother—Brother Gilbert."

Then he told me that I was to go with him, that I would be given a fine home and taught things that would make me into a useful citizen. I didn't want to go. I liked the freedom of the street; liked the gang of youngsters I played with.

But I went.

For a while I wasn't happy. I missed the crowds, and the dirt, and the noise of the street. I missed the other kids. I even missed the policemen. As I look back at it now I realize that I must have been a real problem to the Brothers.

But Brother Gilbert stuck with me. I owe him a lot. More than I'll ever be able to repay.

It was Brother Gilbert who finally struck upon the thing to hold my interest and keep me happy. It was baseball. Once I had been introduced to school athletics, I was satisfied and happy. Even as a kid I was big for my years, and because of my size I used to get most any job I liked on the team. Sometimes I pitched. Sometimes I caught, and frequently I played the outfield and in-

field. It was all the same to me. All I wanted was to play. I didn't care where.

As I grew older, Brother Gilbert encouraged me more and more. At sixteen I had developed into a pretty good catcher and was beginning to hit pretty well. I was tall and skinny in those days. From some of the pictures that still hang on the walls over at school, I guess I must have been about as funny-looking a kid as ever got a trouncing for cutting classes to go fishing.

There were a lot of fine men connected with the school. They are among the very few people who call me "George." To the rest of the world, and particularly to the baseball fans, I'm "Babe" and have been ever since I broke into baseball. The coach of the Baltimore Orioles gave me the nickname when I joined the club in 1914. Jack Dunn, owner and manager of the club, had sent me over. The first day I reported at the clubhouse, the coach said, "Well, here's Jack's newest babe now."

And the name stuck. I suppose I will still be "Babe" when I'm an old, old man with wobbly legs and long whiskers.

Brother Gilbert was responsible for my getting a chance to get into league baseball. He used to coach our baseball team, and he liked the way I did things. Lots of times he would point me out as an example to the other boys, as a baseball player, you understand; and finally, when I was eighteen, he wrote a letter to Jack Dunn telling him about me.

I'll never forget the day Brother Gilbert called me over and introduced me to Jack. I was flabbergasted. I hadn't known about the letter, and the idea of shaking hands with a real professional baseball man was almost too much. Jack was mighty good to me and talked for quite a while about baseball. Finally he got me into a uniform and out in the yard. He had me pitch to him for a half hour, I guess, talking to me all the time, and telling me not to strain and not to try too hard. I was a pretty fair pitcher in those days, if I do say so myself. At the end of a half hour, Dunn called a halt and went into the office with Brother Gilbert.

In about another half hour they called me in. Brother Gilbert explained that Mr. Dunn thought I would make a ball player, and wanted me to sign a contract with the Baltimore Orioles.

"How about it, young man," Dunn asked me, "do you want to play baseball?"

I guess I must have come near falling over in my excitement. Did I want to play baseball? Does a fish like to swim or a squirrel climb trees? I didn't even pause to ask questions.

"Sure," I said, "I'll play. When do I start?"

But Brother Gilbert stopped me.

"Wait a minute, George," he said, "this is a serious business. Boys play baseball for fun, but you're a man now and you're taking a man's job. You know playing professional baseball isn't like playing on the sand lots. The men on the Baltimore team know a

BABE RUTH'S OWN STORY

lot more baseball than you do.
It won't be easy. Besides, I want
you to understand all the arrangements. Mr. Dunn has agreed to
pay you six hundred dollars for
the six-months' season. That's
about twenty-five dollars a week.
Will you be satisfied with that?"

Twenty-five dollars a week!
Why I'd be as rich as Rockefeller,
I thought. And for playing base-
ball! I never even hesitated.

"Sure, I'd like it," I said, and
said it fast too, for fear Dunn
might change his mind. And so
it was arranged. A contract was
drawn up, and I signed it. Then
I beat it out-of-doors to tell the
rest of the boys.

In the years that have gone by
I've had a lot of thrills. I got one
when I pitched my first world
series game. I get one every time
I hit a ball over the fence, and I
got a big one that day when I hit
my sixtieth home run and broke
my old record. But none of these
could compare to the thrill that
came the day I paraded out to the
playground and told the boys that
I was signed to a contract.

Adapted from *Babe Ruth's Own Book of Baseball*

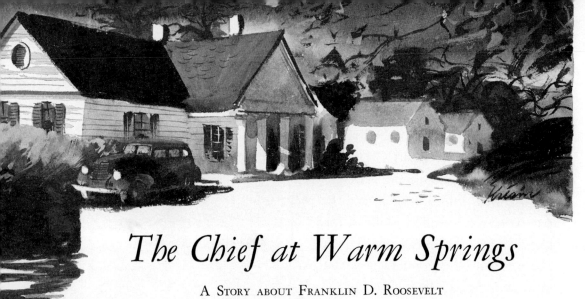

The Chief at Warm Springs

A STORY ABOUT FRANKLIN D. ROOSEVELT

By ANN WEIL

IN THE spring of 1933 a little girl pushed herself across a lawn in Warm Springs, Georgia. She had had infantile paralysis, and was still a patient at the Warm Springs hospital. Her face was flushed. Her eyes were bright with excitement.

"Yoo-hoo, Jimmy!" she called to a boy who was pushing himself along in a wheel chair. "Jimmy!" she called again. "I've the most wonderful news. Guess who's coming!"

Jimmy was a new patient at the hospital. He was homesick and discouraged. Only a few weeks before he had been running and playing like other boys. Now all he could do was push himself along in a wheel chair. Nancy's enthusiasm didn't interest him.

"I don't care who's coming," he said. "What difference does it make anyway?"

"You won't say that when I tell you," Nancy said. "Oh, Jimmy, I just heard. President Franklin Delano Roosevelt is coming. Just think, you're going to see the President of the United States!"

Even this news failed to arouse Jimmy. "What's he coming for?" he asked. "Because he feels sorry for us? I don't want anyone feeling sorry for me. Not even the President of the United States."

"But, Jimmy, why should he feel sorry for us?"

"Why?" Jimmy looked at her in amazement. Then, without a

word, he looked down at his own crippled legs.

"But, Jimmy," Nancy said, "there's no reason why he should be sorry for us any more than we should feel sorry for him."

"What?" Jimmy stared at her. "Are you crazy? Why on earth should you and I feel sorry for the President?"

"Jimmy—" now it was Nancy's turn to be surprised—"don't you know? Don't you know that President Roosevelt has infantile paralysis, too?"

At first Jimmy was too amazed to say anything. After a few minutes, he shook his head slowly from side to side. "No, Nancy," he said, "I didn't know. I guess it's strange, but I didn't know. Did he get it when he was young, too?"

"No." Nancy was pleased that Jimmy had finally become interested in something besides himself. "Listen," she said, "I'll tell you all about it. He became ill when he was thirty-nine years old. Both his legs were completely paralyzed.

"The doctors weren't sure they could help him. You know, it's harder to cure a grownup. They told him it would take years of patient exercise and many painful treatments. Even then they didn't know whether they would be able to help him. And, Jimmy, do you know what he said? He said, 'When does the work begin? If there's any way to beat this thing I'm going to do it.'

"For three years he did everything the doctors told him to do. Bit by bit he became better. It took him almost two years to learn how to move one toe. Finally he could move one foot. Then, months later, he was able to move both of them. At last, with the help of braces and crutches, he was able to swing himself along.

"Then—" Nancy's eyes grew bright—"he heard that some people had been helped by bathing in the waters here at Warm Springs. So he decided to come here, too. And guess what happened, Jimmy! He made more progress here in six weeks than he had in all the three years before.

"This was just a tiny place then, with a few old cottages. Mr. Roosevelt decided to enlarge it, so that many people might come here for treatment. Before long he had started the Warm Springs Foundation, and—well, look at it now! Look at all the wonderful buildings we have here today."

Jimmy nodded. Nancy's eyes were brighter than ever now. "Guess what," she said. "One day when he was swimming right over there in that swimming pool he got a telephone call. He was asked to run for Governor of New York State. He said he wouldn't do it, but they nominated him anyway. And he won the election! In 1932 he won another election. Then he became the President of the United States."

Jimmy looked up at Nancy and smiled. "Do you think I'll really get to see him when he comes?" he asked.

"See him? Why, of course, you will. You'll see him many times. And that's what I came over here to tell you. You're going to see him tonight. He's having dinner with us in the main dining room. Afterward we'll all sing songs together. We always do. Somehow, as soon as he gets here, we all forget that he's the President of the United States. We call him the Chief."

142

THE CHIEF AT WARM SPRINGS

"Nancy—" Jimmy spoke slowly, as though he were talking to himself—"you know, Nancy, I don't feel the same way I did a little while ago. I thought my life was spoiled. I didn't think I'd ever be able to do anything interesting or important. I thought everyone would feel sorry for me and—well, I don't feel that way any more. Gee!" He looked at Nancy and laughed. "I'm starved. I hope the Chief isn't late for dinner."

. . . . .

In the fall of 1946 Jimmy and his father stood on the steps of President Roosevelt's Hyde Park home. President Roosevelt had died the year before. Now the house belonged to the Government. It was a public museum.

Jimmy walked up to the door. His legs were strong and straight now. He had almost forgotten that he had had infantile paralysis.

"We're too early, Father," he said. "It's only nine-thirty. The sign says that visiting hours are from ten until five."

"We can sit down over there on the bench while we're waiting," his father answered. "It will be nice to watch the birds. I've never seen so many in one place."

They sat down, and for a while neither of them said anything. But Jimmy, who was always full of questions, couldn't keep quiet for long.

"Don't you think President Roosevelt was one of our greatest Presidents?" he asked.

"Yes," his father answered. "I certainly do."

"What do you think was his greatest accomplishment?" Jimmy went on.

Jimmy's father smiled. "That is hard to decide," he said. "He led the country through a great war. But he did many other important things. Everyone you ask would have a different answer. And," he added, "some people don't think he was great at all."

Jimmy nodded and his father went on.

"No President can please everyone. America is a very large country. What pleases one group of people often displeases another group. But President Roosevelt worked hard for the ideas he thought were right. He wanted four freedoms for all people everywhere in the world. Freedom from want. Freedom from fear. Freedom to worship in the way each person thinks is right. Freedom of speech."

The front door opened and the caretaker looked out. "You may come in now," he said.

Jimmy and his father started up the steps. Then they stopped and looked at the house again before they went inside. It was a nice house. It was a big, old-fashioned, comfortable American home. This was the house where Franklin Delano Roosevelt was born. This was the house he loved, the house to which he always returned.

Here he had had freedom from want, freedom from fear, freedom to worship as he pleased, freedom to say the things he thought were right. Here he had hoped and planned and worked.

From *Franklin Roosevelt, Boy of the Four Freedoms*

The Feast of Eat-Everything

By H. E. MARSHALL

THE early story of Canada is full of the brave deeds of the 'Black Robes,' as the Indians called the priests.

In 1642 Montreal was founded at the place which, a hundred years before, Cartier had called Mount Royal. It was founded, not by traders, but by men with the devotion of saints and the spirit of martyrs. Some of these brave priests went far into the country, among the tribe called the Huron, teaching them to be Christians. For many years they lived and worked among them. But the Iroquois, who were the deadly enemies of French and Huron alike, waged war against these missions. They plundered and killed, burned and tortured, until the Huron as a nation were destroyed.

The Iroquois were fierce, and strong, and treacherous. They did not care what means they used, so long as their enemies were tortured and killed. Now, the Iroquois pretended that they would be pleased if some of the Black Robes would come to live among

them, and teach them as they had taught the Hurons. The French could hardly believe that these fierce enemies really wanted to be taught. But they were glad at the thought of peace, and about fifty brave men, ten only of whom were soldiers, decided to go and live among the Iroquois.

They were received with much joy. The savages danced and feasted, smoked the pipe of peace, sang songs, and made speeches, and pretended to be so glad that one of the priests said, 'If after this they murder us, it will be from changeableness and not from treachery.' But he little knew the blackness of the Iroquois heart.

Soon the forest rang with the sound of ax and hammer as the Frenchmen, priest and soldier alike, worked side by side to build their new homes.

Days and weeks went past; the priests who had gone to live

THE FEAST OF EAT-EVERYTHING

among the Iroquois taught, and worked, and prayed. In the great forest this handful of white men lived alone among the prowling savages, 'who came like foxes, fought like lions, and disappeared like birds'—but, strong in their faith, they had no fear.

At length, however, dark whispers of treachery came to them. Friendly Indians warned them that the chiefs had met in council, and had vowed to kill them all. The Black Robes found it hard to believe that the men who treated them with such smiling kindness meant to kill them. But they were not left long in doubt, for a dying Indian, repenting of his treachery, told them all the plot. Every man was to be killed before the spring.

The Frenchmen now knew that they must escape, and quickly. But how? All day long the Indians strolled about, following every step of the Frenchmen, watching their every movement, in make-believe friendliness. At night they slept around the gate of the mission, ready to spring awake at the slightest sound. To try to escape through the forest was impossible. There was but one hope, and that was to cross the lake near which the mission was built, and sail down the river to Montreal. But to do this they needed boats, and they had only eight canoes, which were not nearly enough to carry them all.

The Frenchmen were desperate, but not hopeless. Over the mis-

sion-house there was a large loft. There the Indians seldom came,
and there the priests began in secret to build two large boats. They
were soon ready. The next thing was to find, or make, a chance
to use them.

Among the Frenchmen was a young man of whom the Indian
chief had become very fond. One morning he went to the chief
pretending to be in great trouble. 'I have had a dream, my father,'
he said. 'It has been shown to me by the Great Spirit that I shall
certainly die. Nothing can save me but a magic feast.'

The Indians believed very much in dreams. They thought that
those who did not do as dreams told them would be sorely punished.
So the chief at once replied: 'Thou art my son. Thou shalt not die.
We shall have a feast, and we shall eat every morsel.'

These magic feasts were called Feasts of Eat-Everything. At
them, each guest was bound to eat all that was set before him. No
matter how much he had eaten, no matter how ill he felt, he was

148

bound to go on until the person whose feast it was said he might
stop.

As soon as the day was fixed, the priests set to work with right
good will to make a great feast. They killed their pigs; they
brought the nicest things out of their stores; they made the most
tempting dishes. But the chief thing they thought of was to have
a great quantity of food.

The evening came. Great fires were lit around the mission-
house. The Indians gathered about them. First there were games,
dances, and songs. One game was to see who could make the most
noise by screaming and yelling. The Frenchmen gave a prize to
whoever could yell loudest, so that the savages tired themselves out
trying to win the prize. At last, worn out with their efforts, they
all sat down in a circle. Great steaming pots were brought from
the fires, and each man's wooden basin was filled. As soon as the
basins were empty, they were filled, again and yet again. The

Indians were hungry, and they ate greedily. While they stuffed themselves, the Frenchmen beat drums, blew trumpets, and sang songs, making as much noise as they could. This they did to cover any strange sound that might come from the shade of the forest to the sharp ears of the savages. For, in the darkness, beyond the glare of the firelight, a few white men were straining every muscle to carry the heavy boats unseen and unheard to the lake. With beating hearts and held breath, now stopping fearfully, now hurrying onward, they reached the lake. The boats were safely launched.

The hours went on, and still the feast did not end. The gorged savages could eat no more. 'Is it not enough?' they cried. 'Have pity on us and let us rest.'

'Nay,' replied the young Frenchman, 'you must eat everything. Would you see me die?'

And, although the Indians meant to kill him, perhaps the very next day, they still ate on, for this was a magic feast. It had been ordered in a dream by the Great Spirit whom they must obey. Making strange faces, rolling their eyes wildly, choking, gulping, they ate till they could not move.

'That will do,' said the young man at last. 'You have saved my life. Now you may sleep. And do not rise early tomorrow. Rest till we come to waken you for prayers. Now we will play sweet music to send you to sleep.'

Stupid with over-eating, dazed with drink, the savages slept. Meanwhile the priests had fastened the doors and windows of the mission-house, and locked the gate in the high fence that surrounded it. Then one by one they glided stealthily to the boats, until the last man was safe aboard.

It was March and still very cold, and now snow began to fall so that their footprints were covered over.

The lake was still lightly frozen over, and, as the first boat

pushed off, men leaned from the bow and broke the ice with hatchets.
The rowers pulled with all their strength, forcing the boat through
the shattered ice. The second boat followed in its track. Last of all
came the canoes. Thus they crossed the lake, and, reaching the river,
were soon carried swiftly downstream. On and on they went through
the dark night, fleeing from death, and from torture worse than
death. When the sun rose, shedding pale wintry gleams on dark
forest and swift-flowing stream, they were far away.

All through the night the Indians slept their sleep of gluttony.
When they awoke, late in the morning, they still felt dull and stupid.
But, arousing themselves at last, they found that all around was still
and silent. No sound came from the mission-house, no smoke rose
from its chimney. What could it mean?

Full of curiosity, the Indians pressed their faces against the fence,
trying to see through the cracks in the wood. There was nothing to
see. A dog barked in the house; a cock crowed in the yard. All else

THE FEAST OF EAT-EVERYTHING

about the mission was still.

At last, impatient to know what was happening within, the Indians climbed the fence, burst open the door, and entered the house. It was empty.

Great was the anger of the savages, greater still their astonishment. How could the Black Robes have escaped? they asked themselves. They had no boats, so they could not escape by water. There was no trace of them on land, so they had not escaped by the forest. There was only one explanation. This was the work of the Great Spirit. The Black Robes and their followers had flown away through the air during the night. And, with this thought, fear fell upon the heart of the Red Man.

Meanwhile, the Black Robes were speeding on their way down the river. On and on they went, hardly pausing for rest, until a month later they reached Quebec. They were saved through the Feast of Eat-Everything.

From *Canada's Story*

The King of the Fur Traders

By Donald J. Dickie and Helen Palk

PIERRE Radisson was fifteen when he came with his family to Canada, and settled in Three Rivers.

One day Pierre went out with two friends to shoot ducks. When they had gone a little way from the fort the friends, in fear of the Iroquois, turned back. Radisson, laughing at them, went on till he had shot more fowl than he could carry. He hid some in a hollow tree, and started home after the others.

When halfway there, he found his two friends dead upon the ground. In another moment, he was surrounded by yelling Iroquois. He fired at them, but someone tripped him. He fell flat upon the ground and was quickly made prisoner.

Seeing him so young and brave, the Indians were pleased. They of-

fered him some of their meat. But the meat smelled so horribly that Radisson could not make himself eat it, so the Indians cooked some fresh for him.

The Iroquois now traveled slowly homeward, often stopping to hunt. Radisson laughed, joked, and sang French songs for them. "Often," says he, "have I sunged in French, to which they gave eares with a deepe silence." They trimmed his hair and greased it in Iroquois fashion.

When they reached their village, the other prisoners were made to run the gauntlet, and Radisson expected nothing less for himself; but, as he was about to start, an old squaw came, took him by the hand and led him to her wigwam. She and her husband adopted him in place of their son, who had been killed. Their son's name had been Orimha, which means "a stone." When they found out that Radisson's name was Pierre, which also means "a stone," they were very happy. They felt sure the Great Spirit had sent Pierre to them to replace their lost boy. They called him Orimha, and did everything they could for him.

Radisson stayed with his Iroquois parents nearly two years. At last he had a chance to escape. He fled to the Dutch Settlement on the Atlantic Coast. As soon as he could, he made his way back to Three Rivers, where his people had long given him up for dead.

One person who listened with great interest to the story of Radisson's strange adventure was his brother-in-law, Groseilliers, who was also a trader.

THE KING OF THE FUR TRADERS

Neither of these adventurous young men thought, however, of settling down at Three Rivers. Both were anxious to learn more of the vast territory that extended northwest and north to unknown waters.

During their wanderings, they heard much from the Indians of the "Great Bay of the North." "There," said the Indians, "the beaver are as plentiful as rabbits." Radisson was eager to discover this "Great Bay." He had sprained his ankle badly; but, in spite of it, he started out with a party of Indians to go there. Whether or not he reached it, no one is quite sure, but it is certain that he learned a great deal about it.

In the autumn, he and Groseilliers returned to Montreal with three hundred and sixty canoes loaded with beaver skins. This was the largest load of furs that had ever been brought down from the upper lakes. "The great number of our boats," says Radisson, "did almost cover the whole river." The merchants of Montreal and Quebec had been very short of beaver skins. They gave the traders a rousing welcome.

Radisson and Groseilliers felt sure that the Governor would be pleased with what they had done. They expected to be rewarded for their discoveries, and honored for the splendid load of furs they had brought in. Instead of that, the Governor put Groseilliers in prison for going to the lakes without his permission. He made them pay half the value of their furs as a fine. This made them very angry.

When they were free, Radisson and Groseilliers left Quebec and New France. They fled to the English town of Boston. Here they met the Royal Commissioners of Charles II, who were in America on business for their king. When the Commissioners heard from the Frenchmen of the "Great Bay of the North," where beaver skins were as thick as blueberries, they persuaded the venturesome traders to return with them to England.

When they arrived in England, Groseilliers and Radisson were presented to King Charles, who received them graciously. The King and the ladies and gentlemen of the Court listened eagerly to the thrilling stories of adventure told by the Frenchmen. King Charles remembered that great bay which had been found and claimed for England by Henry Hudson. He coveted the rich furs which could be found there, but he did not want to spend the money at that time.

But there was a gentleman of the Court who was even more interested than the King. This was Prince Rupert, the gallant, dash-

ing cousin of King Charles. He was very anxious to have a share
in any expedition that might be formed. He soon interested a number of his friends, who promised to pay the sailors' wages and provide
their food. The merchants of London were only too glad to send
some of their goods to trade. King Charles ordered a ship, the *Eaglet,*
to be given to them, and the gentlemen themselves equipped another,
the *Nonsuch.*

When the ships were ready on June 3, 1668, Prince Rupert and
the "Adventurers" inspected the stores and the crew. In Captain Gil-
lam's cabin, on the *Nonsuch,* they drank to the success of the voyage, and, as the Prince and his companions rowed ashore, the two
little vessels weighed anchor and set sail for Hudson's Bay.

In mid-ocean, a storm came up. The ships lost one another.
When it was over, the *Eaglet* was so badly crippled that Radisson,
who was sailing in her, had to put back to London.

Meanwhile, the little *Nonsuch,* with Groseilliers, continued its course, and, in spite of heavy storms, reached the Bay in safety. It passed to the south of James Bay, which was reached on September 29. A palisaded fort was built and named Fort Charles, after the English king. Here the voyagers spent a long and dreary winter. By April, the ice swept out of the river with a roar, and by June it was summer again.

Groseilliers had been doing an active trade with the Indians, and the *Nonsuch* sailed to England loaded with a rich cargo of furs.

Now, indeed, there was no more trouble in getting ships or money. The merchants, the courtiers, Prince Rupert, King Charles himself, all were eager to have a share in the new fur trade.

A company was formed, and Prince Rupert with Groseilliers and Radisson went to ask King Charles for a Charter. This was granted on May 2, 1670, to Prince Rupert and his friends, who became "The Governor and Company of Adventurers of England Trading into Hudson's Bay." To this Company were given the lands whose waters emptied into Hudson's Bay, and also the sole rights of trade and commerce in these wide regions.

In 1671, Groseilliers and Radisson were again at the Bay. Other forts were established, and rich cargoes of furs went back each year to London. This was the beginning of the Hudson's Bay Company, which later ruled the stretch of country known as Rupert's Land, and which established the great fur centers of the North.

From *Pages from Canada's Story*

Alexander Graham Bell

By George E. Tait

ON March 10, 1876, an event occurred in a Boston, Mass., rooming house which changed the social and business habits of the world.

An intense young man leaned over a cluttered table as he worked with wire, tools, and a crude type of transmitter. In his haste he overturned a battery, causing the acid to splatter over his clothing.

He looked annoyed and exasperated. "Mr. Watson," he called, "come here. I want you."

A wildly excited electrician burst into the room. "Mr. Bell," he sputtered, "I heard every word you said distinctly."

Bell's eyes opened wide. "By the receiver?" he demanded.

"Certainly. I heard every word!"

"At last!" beamed Bell, turning to pat the transmitter.

Bell's summer vacation in 1874 had been spent at his father's home in Brantford, in the Canadian province of Ontario. For hours he discussed with his father the progress of his experiments, and was encouraged by the interest and excitement of the older man. The thoughts, inspiration, and discussions arising from that particular vacation gave Alexander Bell his first idea of broadening his experiments to search for a method of transmitting the human voice.

After he returned to Boston, he and Watson continued their patient and careful work which reached a climax in the spectacular success of the evening when Bell spilled the acid on his clothes and shouted for help.

Bell and Watson were convinced that their equipment was satisfactory for short distances, but could the human voice be made to carry over the miles? During the next summer, Bell was back in Brantford and took this opportunity to make his first distance test. Utilizing a commercial telegraph line running from Paris to Brantford, he attached his receiver in one city and the transmitter in the other. On August 10, 1876, Bell listened at the receiver in Paris and heard his father's voice speaking from Brantford!

The efficiency of the primitive telephone had been proved. A new age of communication was dawning on a world still unaware of the great discovery.

In the United States and in England, Bell gave numerous lectures and conducted many demonstrations of his equipment, foretelling with remarkable accuracy the effect his telephone would have on human activity.

In 1915, Bell enjoyed still another thrill when he spoke into a telephone located in New York City. His words were the same historical message he had uttered thirty-nine years previously:

"Mr. Watson, come here. I want you."

There was a breathless moment of silence, and then came a familiar voice from San Francisco.

"I would be glad to come, but it will take a week."

Bell and Watson had spoken across the entire continent of America! The great day of the telephone had come.

From *Famous Canadian Stories*

Louis Braille, The Boy
Who Brought Light to the Blind

By Elizabeth Flugaur

LOUIS heard strange sounds as he walked through the streets of Paris, holding tightly to his father's hand. Wagons rumbled across the cobblestones, and horses stamped by in the bustling city. It had not been like this in the quiet little village of Coupvrai, France, where he lived.

Monsieur Braille looked down at his ten-year-old son. "Soon we will be there, Louis," he said. Louis nodded happily. They were on their way to the school the priest had told Louis so much about.

"There you would learn many things that we cannot teach you at home," the priest had said. Louis had listened intently as the priest told him more about this school for blind boys. It seemed to Louis a new world was opening to him, for he, too, was blind.

Louis had lived in darkness since he was three years old. He had been playing with a sharp instrument in his father's leather shop. Suddenly it had slipped and gone into his eye. The injury had caused Louis to lose the sight in both eyes. He knew that he would never see again.

Louis was an intelligent boy and anxious to learn. He was happy over the new opportunity open to him at the Paris school. He had

161

heard about the new way of reading by raised letters taught there.
"Now," he said, "I will learn to
read."

As Louis and his father entered
the school, Louis heard sounds of
children playing in the next room
—children who were blind like
himself. He began to feel at home.

Then he felt the friendly hand-
clasp of the man who introduced
himself as Monsieur Valentin
Haüy, the founder of the school.
Louis felt he was in the presence
of a great man.

So Louis began his new life at
the school. He soon got over his
first homesickness, as he became
acquainted with his teachers and
classmates and his new surroundings.

desk. But as he worked in the darkness and stillness of the night, he knew that someday his work would bring help and light for the blind. And it did.

After many years, Louis developed a successful code. It consisted of the alphabet made up of different arrangements of dots, in groups of from one to six. One dot is A; two dots, one on top of the other, are B; two dots side by side are C, and so on. The dots are made by pressing a sharp, pencillike tool into a heavy piece of paper. The paper is then turned over so that the raised dots can be felt on the other side.

Certain symbols and various changes make it possible to use this system for other purposes. It even can be used to read music. Because of Louis Braille's system, blind children today can read and write almost as fast as children who can see.

So Louis Braille's own loss of sight was turned into a great usefulness for blind people everywhere. He lived before the Civil War. But he will be remembered always for his system of reading and writing known by his name—Braille.

Adapted by permission from *Highlights for Children,* Columbus, Ohio.

T.P. and Jake

By Thomas Hart Benton

I N THIS *story, the artist himself tells us of a dog's love for a boy,*
which inspired him to paint the picture shown.

      Rita found Jake on a farm west of Kansas City. The farmer
who owned him said: "If you'll give that dog a good home you can
have him." So he was brought to our house.

T.P., our boy, who was then eight years old, was delighted. So
was the dog, but because he had never been in a house he was a little
gawky and clumsy, and slid on the rugs. He was named Jake because
he was a country dog, a country jake, who hadn't learned city ways.

Jake sat with T.P. in the back seat of our car on the trips from
Kansas City to the summers on Martha's Vineyard, Massachusetts. He
was fascinated by the speeding world out the window. He would sit
upright, his tongue rolling out of his laughing face, his ears erect, and
with the spit of well-tasted pleasure dripping off his lips.

On Menemsha pond T.P. had a rowboat. He rigged this up with
a homemade mast and a three-cornered red sail and called it the *Red*

Jacket. It was supposed to be a pirate ship. Every afternoon T.P. and Jake would board this vessel and sail the pond. Jake would bark at the gulls. If he got tired of this, he'd jump overboard and swim to land. Then he'd bark at T.P. from the shore, running up and down, full of a tense glory of life.

After three years, Rita took T.P. to Italy to visit his grandmother. This was a sad time for Jake. Up to now he'd given me little attention. Now, however, he clung to me, until the day I took him to the docks in New York to meet the boat returning his real master.

There was a high rail between the passageway for passengers and the people who had come to meet them. I stood by this fence trying to

catch a glimpse of Rita and T.P. But Jake beat me to it. The chain leash in my hand twisted suddenly, and, before I knew it, Jake's seventy pounds of muscle and tawny hair was soaring over the fence.

No one who saw that meeting of boy and dog could ever forget it. The travelers and those who met them stood aside to watch the play of Jake's ecstasy. His yaps of joy sailed up over the arching girders to the high roofs of the pier sheds and came back to pierce your heart. This was a high point of life, and those who saw, recognized it.

Story adapted by permission of Thomas Hart Benton and the *Vineyard Gazette*.

The Story of Madame Curie

By Alice Thorne

MARIE walked briskly along the dark, wintry street. She was thinking of the happy summer months she had spent at home with her father and other relatives. And she was thinking, too, of a scholarship she had won for university study.

"Six hundred rubles!" she thought happily. This was about three hundred dollars. "Without that money I could never have come back to the Sorbonne for a second year. The mathematics course I am taking seems terribly hard. But then, so did physics, at first."

She stopped at a crossing to let a horse-drawn cart pass noisily on the cobble-stoned street. Then, turning up her coat collar, she shivered a little and hurried on her way to visit some Polish friends.

When she reached the boardinghouse in which her friends were staying, she found another guest there before her. He was a young

Adapted from *The Story of Madame Curie* by Alice Ehorne, copyright 1959, by permission of Grosset and Dunlap, Inc.

scientist named Pierre Curie.

Pierre Curie was a tall man, a few years older than Marie. He had fine hands and honest, peaceful eyes. His slow, friendly smile made Marie like him at once.

The four young people sat down near the balcony window, through which the lights of Paris twinkled. They drank tea and talked science. Pierre Curie was amazed at how much this beautiful young Polish student knew.

"Are you going to make France your home?" he asked her.

"Oh, no," Marie replied. "I shall take my mathematics examination this summer. Then, if I can manage it, I'll come back for one more year. After that, I shall become a teacher in Poland. We need teachers there."

"But you would not be able to continue your scientific studies in Poland," Pierre objected. Even as he said the words, he knew what he really meant: he did not want Marie to leave France—ever.

In the spring months that followed their meeting, Pierre gently persuaded Marie to see him more and more often. By July, she had passed her mathematics examination and was about to go home to Warsaw. Pierre asked her to stay in Paris and marry him. But Marie could not bear the thought of leaving her family and Poland forever. She promised only that she would try to return to Paris in the fall.

Marie kept that promise. Bringing her home from a day in the country, Pierre said:

"If I were to leave Paris, go to Poland, and get a position there, *then* would you marry me? I could give French lessons, and we could do scientific work whenever we had the time."

"Pierre, how can you think of such a thing?" Marie exclaimed. "You are a genius. You must never give up your work here in Paris."

Marie meant what she said. And in the same moment, she realized she could no longer bear the thought of being away from Pierre.

On July 26, 1895, Marie and Pierre were married. They both

continued their scientific experiments. Marie continued to work in their laboratory even after their baby daughter was born.

One Sunday morning Pierre said, "Today, I am going to the 'lab' with you."

"You are?" Marie exclaimed in pleased surprise. "But on Sunday you always work on the crystals in the—"

Pierre laughed. "I don't believe you quite realize the importance of your work even now, Marie," he said. "But other scientists do. One of them has even written an article about the unknown element you think you may have discovered in pitchblende ore. So I've decided to stop my experiments with crystals for a while, and help you try to find it."

"Pierre, that is wonderful!" Marie said, as she started to dress the baby.

Soon they were ready, and the tall, bearded young man and the slender, blond young woman strolled down the street. Marie was pushing the baby in the carriage, and they looked like any other young couple taking an early morning walk. But what they talked about was quite different. For Marie and Pierre already were planning how they would work together in Marie's little laboratory.

From then on, it was "We found," or "We observed," in all their notebooks and reports. By July, Marie and Pierre were sure that there was not just one unknown element in pitchblende ore. There were two.

When they finally succeeded in chemically separating one of the new elements, Pierre said to Marie, "You must name it."

Marie thought a moment. Then she suggested, "Could we call it —polonium?"

Pierre smiled. He knew that in selecting that name, Marie was thinking of her beloved Poland.

By December, the two young scientists were able to announce that they had located the second unknown element for which they

had been searching.

They called it radium.

But it was one thing to say that radium existed. It was quite another thing to convince the scientists who were watching Marie and Pierre's work with keen interest. If there really was such a thing as radium, these men argued, then they wanted to see it, and to weigh it.

"We shall have to produce salts of actual radium," Marie said to Pierre.

Pierre nodded. Then he added, "But that means we'll need a lot of pitchblende ore, tons of it. We can never afford to buy it—Wait a minute!" he exclaimed. "You mentioned once that at the mines in Austria they take out the uranium to use in making glass. What is left of the pitchblende is of no use to the miners. Perhaps we can get hold of some of it cheaply. Let's try."

Once Marie and Pierre had decided on a plan, they wasted no

time in carrying it out. And one morning a big wagon loaded with burlap sacks filled with pitchblende pulled up in the courtyard of the School of Physics. Marie and Pierre rushed out to the wagon.

"Oh, do cut the string and open one of the sacks," Marie begged Pierre, "so we can look at our pitchblende."

Laughing at her excitement, Pierre opened one of the sacks. Delightedly Marie thrust her hand in and pulled out a fistful of the dull, brownish ore. In the meantime, Pierre told the driver to unload the sacks and take them into a shed on the opposite side of the courtyard.

This old shed was the only place they had been able to find that was big enough to work in. It had an earth floor and flaking plaster walls. When it rained, the roof leaked. The only heat was provided by a rusty old iron stove. But it did have a blackboard, some old tables, and a dusty skylight in the roof.

Marie and Pierre had moved their equipment from the little workroom to the shed. Now they were eager to start work. They might not have felt so eager if they had known it was going to take forty-five months of back-breaking labor to find what they sought.

Day after day Marie stood in the windy courtyard of the school, stirring with a long iron rod the boiling chemicals which she hoped someday would yield salts of radium. She mixed chemicals, and she separated them, filling great jars with strange-looking substances which she and Pierre would study.

After nearly three years, even Pierre, who worked inside the shed, became discouraged.

"Marie, Marie," he exclaimed one day, when she had stopped work long enough to come indoors and drink a cup of tea with him. "You cannot go on like this. It will take years to try to prepare radium in this old shed, which is always either too hot or too cold. You may never get it. Why not give up this operation and simply continue your study of radioactivity?"

"No," Marie said stubbornly, "I will keep on until I get our radium. I wonder what it will be like," she added dreamily.

"Perhaps it will have a beautiful color," Pierre said, smiling.

"I must get it, I must . . ." Marie murmured.

On a May evening in 1902, Marie and Pierre walked home from the shed in the gathering twilight. They had worked hard all day, but their heads were high, and their steps were light. Little Irene, four years old now, came running to meet them. "Mé, Mé," she called, her baby way of saying, "Mother," and flung herself into her mother's arms.

Marie hugged the child, and taking her hand, went into the house. Soon she had supper on the table, and the little family sat down to eat. Old Doctor Curie, who lived with Marie and Pierre, had tied a bib on Irene, and the little girl was busy picking the "pearls" out of her tapioca pudding.

Marie looked across the table at Pierre. Her gray eyes were sparkling. Pierre turned to his father, who sat opposite Irene.

"Father," Pierre said, "Marie has something to tell you. Something we want you to know before anyone else knows."

"Yes?" The old doctor looked at Marie curiously. "What is it, my dear?"

"We have done it!" Marie announced triumphantly. "We have finally obtained—salts of radium!"

"Marie! My congratulations to you both!" old Doctor Curie exclaimed. He rose from his chair and came and kissed Marie on both cheeks. Then he embraced his son also.

THE STORY OF MADAME CURIE

Soon after supper, Marie put Irene to bed. At last Irene was asleep. Pierre's father went to bed early also. When Marie came back to the living room, she found Pierre prowling around restlessly. Marie sat down in the old mahogany armchair and began to sew on an apron she was making for Irene. But she could not keep her mind on her sewing, and pricked her finger twice. Finally she put down her work and looked at Pierre.

"Shall we go back—" she began.

"Yes, let's," he agreed. She did not need to finish her sentence. Both were longing to return to the "lab."

In the dingy school courtyard once again, Pierre pushed open the squeaky door of the old shed. They walked into the dark workroom.

But now the old shed had become beautiful. For in the darkness, like the luminous hands of a clock in the night—but far brighter—glowed and shimmered the radiant, bluish fragments of precious radium!

North to Labrador

A Story of Wilfred Grenfell

By May McNeer

GRAY wind-swept clouds scudded across the sky above the coast of England as people ran from their homes, from taverns and fields, toward the Sands of Dee. Two boys joined the fisher-folk, dashing out of the gate of the big house on the hill when their watchful nurse was not looking. Overhead, gulls circled and turned with mournful cries. Wilfred and his brother, Algernon, joined the knot of women, who were making little cries that sounded as sad as the gull songs.

Wilfred had to bite his lips to keep from crying as he saw the boats pulled onto the sands and two young fishermen lifted out. An old doctor came, but shook his head as he knelt beside the men. It was no use, for the cruel sea had drowned them.

The little boys turned and went out along the sands. Wilfred raised his head and took a deep breath of salt air, mixed with the scents of fish and tar, as he looked across the waters toward Wales, on the other side.

He loved the sea, and the sands, and he admired fishermen more than any other men in the world. Here, where Wilfred Grenfell lived with his father, his mother, and his two brothers, people were adventurous. At the age of five, in the year 1870, he decided that he would be a fisherman. The sea took some—but he was sure that it would not take him!

The Grenfells lived near the town of Chester, in England. At first Wilfred went to the school run by his father, who was also a minister. Then his father decided that these two older boys, who were constantly wandering away along the sands, playing in fishing boats and getting into mischief, should go elsewhere. They were sent to different schools—Algernon to Repton and Wilfred to Marlborough.

At Marlborough, Wilfred, a merry, active boy, had to fight for his rights, and he achieved the admired title of "The Beast" because he usually won his battles. He enjoyed athletics, and made more of a name for himself in sports than in his studies. School was fun too, for he liked the boys and they liked him, and yet he missed the sea and the sands, and the slow talk of fishermen.

When Wilfred left school, he went home to live with his father and mother in London and study medicine in the hospital where his father had become chaplain. The hospital was the largest in the British Isles. Wilfred Grenfell worked harder at his studies in London University than ever before. For fun, he helped organize football teams among students and joined the rowing crew of the University, on the Thames River.

When his father died and his mother went to live with relatives outside London, Wilfred moved into an apartment with two other students. In summer he went to the seashore, for the salt water was still home to him, and his happiest times were spent in boats. He and his roommates began to get together groups of slum boys and to take them to the shore for camping trips on the sands. Boys who had never seen the fields and woods and salt water came back to London in the autumn healthier and happier.

In the dark days of winter, fog came down under chimney pots and swirled in brown clouds through the streets of the London slums. Day after day, in the hospital, Wilfred saw the terrible results of poverty. Some of his friends became fashionable doctors, but he was not interested in that kind of life.

In 1886, he passed his examinations and became Doctor Grenfell. More than any others, he still liked seafaring men and enjoyed talking to every fisherman patient who came to the hospital.

Dr. Grenfell joined in plans for a floating hospital and mission for fishing fleets. One cold and stormy January day he sailed to the Dogger Bank in the far North Sea. There were more than twenty thousand men and boys in the herring fleets, fishing on ships that were often covered with ice or snow for months. It took courage to go out to a vessel in a small boat in rough seas, to set a leg or doctor a wound. But the medical and mission ship was a great success.

From his fishermen friends young Doctor Grenfell heard of the fleets that went each year all the long way to the bleak coast of Labrador. Lying north and east of Canada, Labrador was a wild, cold land where only a few fisherfolk, Eskimos, and Indians lived. In all Labrador there was no doctor. Doctor Grenfell felt a deep urge to go there with the fishermen. He searched until he found a little ship that he could buy, and a captain and mate to help him sail it. It was called the *Albert,* and was about the same size as the fifteenth-century vessel that the famous explorer, John Cabot, had sailed along the same sea route in 1497.

The *Albert* reached St. John's Harbour, Newfoundland, just in time to see the town swept by the flames of a devastating fire, and

of starvatic
somebody
started, anc
and doctor:
famous doc

Someho
events of t
MacClanah
turning fro
ested in the
him near th
there. The
that she co
helped with
ciety, which
traveled ab
things goin

The doc
and he ma
man was a
one end of
ways of the
of sled dogs
his rounds
ions. He lil
the doctor
sleep, with
and two ea
out of their
drove his sl
den for his
knew that

just in time for the doctor to rush ashore to help the injured. Wilfred
Grenfell never forgot the quiet courage of these people, who scarcely
allowed the smoking ruins of their town to cool before they started
rebuilding it. The *Albert* was soon off again, following the fishing
fleet to the north along the rocky shores of Labrador. As the doctor's ship dropped anchor in Domino Run, flags were run up on the
fleet's masts, and patients in need of help were already heading for
the *Albert* in small boats.

When he stopped to realize that he was the only doctor, Wilfred
Grenfell felt a bit overwhelmed by his job. As the *Albert* bounced
about on swells, rolling in from the ocean, Grenfell realized that here
was his place. Here he could do a great deal of good for people who
had simple courage, humor, and spirit. Everyone was poor—the Eskimos who came down for the summers from icy lands farther north,
the Indians who appeared silently from inland forests to fish on the
coast, and the English fishermen.

sma
mar
grea
anot

fishe
land
wha
the
in L
it ha
gion
N
retu
few
shor
to le
frien
find
I
he w
Harl
gree
also
went
and
the
mon
Battl
build
L

if necessary, to feed the "doctor's team."

The doctor's team, like other Eskimo dogs, never barked. They howled like their relatives, the wolves, and were even fiercer than wolves. His sled dogs were absolutely fearless and would attack a polar bear, the most ferocious animal of the north, when wolves would not.

As the years passed, the doctor seemed to grow more active, instead of less. Eskimos, known as the "little people," were his friends. He welcomed them in the early summer as they came to the hospital to have their teeth pulled or diseases treated. Doctor Grenfell saw, with sadness, that they frequently died of illnesses from which white men usually recovered without much trouble. Eskimos had always

184

lived on raw seal meat and fish. He knew that the starchy diet of the settlements was not good for them.

Why did the people of Labrador have such a hard time to keep from starving? In this cold land the season was very short for growing things, and most food had to be brought in by traders. Skins and fish should pay enough to keep trappers and fishermen fed and clothed with a roof over them. Yet the people starved. Doctor Grenfell discovered that the reason was the "trucking" system. Traders who owned stores would not use money but, in return for skins or fish, would issue food. After a time the fisherman was always in debt to the storekeeper, and he had to take less for his fish than the catch was worth. What could be done?

Doctor Grenfell started a group of cooperative stores. This gave him some trouble, for the traders fought him. But the doctor was not going to be beaten. After a time the old system changed. Trappers and fishermen were able to get fair prices for their fish and skins, and were better able to stay out of debt.

The years brought honors to Doctor Grenfell. He was knighted by the king of England, and he and his wife became lord and lady. Yet none of the honors meant as much to him as the knowledge that the people of Newfoundland and Labrador had hospitals and schools and the chance for a good life. As long as he lived, he took an active part in the work of the hospital, and a great pride in the friendship of the doctors and nurses who came to help him.

Until Doctor Grenfell died in 1940, his home was on the bare, chilly shores of a northern land far from the Sands of Dee. But here, too, the salt wind swept inland, bringing a scent of ropes, tar, and fish, and overhead gray gulls circled, screaming and crying their sea-bird songs.

Luther Burbank, Plant "Magician"

By Lillian J. Bragdon

IT WAS still early morning when Luther went downstairs. Already his mother was in the kitchen preparing breakfast. Delicious smells of hot bread filled the sunny kitchen. But before he ate he wanted to see if the plants needed watering, and he had to fill the wood boxes.

Each member of the large Burbank family had certain chores to do.

By the time Luther was born—he was the thirteenth child—most of the other Burbank children were grown and away from home. The only time Luther saw them was when they came home for Christmas or holidays. Luther knew that his mother, who was Mr. Burbank's third wife, loved all the children as if they were her own.

Luther stood for a minute watching his mother bustling around the kitchen. Then he gave her a big hug and started out to the woodshed. He would see to the plants after he brought in the wood.

Luther liked to handle the heavy logs of hickory, maple, oak, and apple wood. They smelled so fresh and woodsy. He had to make a great many trips. At last the wood boxes were full. And there was just enough time before breakfast to water the plants.

"Oh, Mother!" he exclaimed as he examined them. "One of the geranium blossoms was leaning on the frosty window and is frozen. I forgot to put a sheet of paper between it and the glass. I'm so sorry. Should I cut it off?"

"Yes. It isn't too serious. The plant isn't hurt," called his mother from the kitchen. "Just pull the plant a little farther away from the cold windowpane. It will soon blossom again. Perhaps you had better carry the cactus to the window in the other room. It will make room for the other plants. Besides, I think it needs more sun."

"All right, I'll do that." Carefully lifting down the cactus plant, Luther started off for the distant window.

This thornless cactus was his special pride. It was almost the first thing he looked at in the morning and the very last he examined before he went to bed. Perhaps because he was still upset about the frozen geranium, or maybe because he was thinking of the warm spring and the buttercups, Luther tripped on the way. The pot slipped from his hands. Down crashed the precious plant. Pot and plant were broken and scattered over the floor.

At first, Luther was too stunned to move. Then he cried, "Mother. Oh, Mother, I've broken the cactus plant."

"Now, Luther, don't get so upset," said his mother, coming in from the kitchen. "I'm sure the plant isn't ruined. We can repot it, and it will grow again. It won't be quite as big for a while, but

time and good care will help. Soon it will be a fine plant again. Now go get another pot and a trowel, and replant it."

Just then Cousin Levi came into the room. "What seems to be the trouble, Luther?" he asked.

"Oh, Cousin Levi, I've broken Mother's beautiful cactus plant, and it will never bloom again."

"Tut-tut, of course it will bloom again," Cousin Levi assured him. "In fact, you can even start a second plant with one of the broken pieces. So stop crying and get me a big pot for the big plant and a small, shallow pot for the new one."

Luther wanted to believe that his cousin knew what he was saying. But he did not understand how the plant could live after such rough treatment.

Cousin Levi mixed some sandy soil with loam and plant food. Then very carefully he cut a broken slab of the thornless cactus and planted it in the soil. Placing the plant in the sunny window, he said, "Don't water it too much. Keep it barely damp. Give it plenty of sun, and before you know it, you will have one more cactus plant. Now let's replant the big one and put it on the windowsill in the other room. Then stop worrying. Someday you'll remember that Cousin Levi and Mother knew what they were talking about."

In the days that followed, Luther did just what Cousin Levi told him to do. And sure enough, soon he had two cactus plants instead of one.

When Luther grew up he moved to California. There, in the

warm climate, he could grow and experiment with plants the year round.

The big cactus plants growing wild in deserts of the Southwest fascinated him. The wild plants had sharp spines. Ranchmen told him that when rain was scarce and crops failed, they would burn off the spines of the cactus plants without hurting the plants and would feed these plants to their cattle. The cacti contained 98 percent water and some nourishment. The cattle seemed to like cactus as food. But burning off the spines was a long and tedious job which ranchmen hated to undertake.

Because of their long spines cacti were almost impossible to handle. However, plants without spines could provide fodder for cattle the year round, Luther reasoned. He remembered the spineless cactus plant he had loved and cared for as a boy in New England. He wondered if he could produce a spineless cactus that would grow and even flourish on arid ground.

So Luther Burbank went to

work. To his surprise, he found that there were a thousand kinds of cactus plants. The first thing to do was to get as many varieties as possible. He collected over six hundred from all parts of the world. These were shipped to him at Santa Rosa at a cost of thousands of dollars. He also hired a crew of men to help him.

Finally he was ready to start his experiments. Slabs of the cacti he had bought were planted, as many as 6,000 a day. At first, Burbank wore gloves to handle them, for the spines were sharp and dangerous. But he found that the gloves slowed the work. So in spite of the fact that millions of cactus needles pierced the skin of his face and hands, he worked without gloves.

Not only were the thorns of tremendous size, but the plants, too, grew big and tall. It was no easy matter to handle the heavy slabs.

As the plants blossomed, Burbank crossed the pollen of one with another by rubbing the stamen of one on the pistil of the other. This had to be done just as soon as the flower began to bloom, before the bees had a chance to get at them. As soon as the fruit appeared and ripened, Burbank cut it open and collected the seeds.

As he worked, he kept careful records so that he knew exactly what each plant was doing. The seeds were carefully planted. Those that did not measure up to what he expected were destroyed. It was most important to pick the right varieties. Burbank wanted to produce plants that not only would have no spines, but that would also have great food value and would grow quickly and without much care.

After years of careful experimentation, he developed a spineless

cactus with all the desired qualities. This plant not only contained 90 per-cent water, but it also had sugar and mineral elements of value to cattle. And what was also important, one acre could produce from 150 to 300 tons of fodder.

In addition to the use of cactus as fodder for cattle, people found the fruit of the variety Burbank developed to be delicious and nutritious. Although some of his cactus pears were not entirely without spines, they were easy to handle. Before long the fruit became popular.

Luther Burbank had solved a fodder problem for cattlemen in the United States. And because cacti slabs of his plants were sold in all parts of the world, cattlemen in other countries grew rich with the crop, too. They were willing to pay big prices for sample plants.

Burbank's enthusiasm, energy, and tireless patience made the "impossible" possible with many kinds of plants. He developed new kinds of potatoes and other vegetables. He loved to work with flowers better than other plants, and he developed our Shasta daisy, a favorite flower with many people. He gave perfume to scentless flowers, flavor to tasteless fruit, and brilliant color to dull flowers.

The people in California proudly called Burbank their green-thumbed wizard and "the great magician." They named a town for him. By the time of his death, in 1926, he was known throughout the world for his "miracles" with plants.

Adapted from *Luther Burbank, Natures Helper* by Lillian Bragdon; copyright © 1959 by Abingdon Press. Used with permission of Abingdon Press, Publishers.

Will Rogers: Immortal Cowboy

By Shannon Garst

WILL could not remember when he had not loved horses and had not wanted to be on top of one. Among his earliest memories was one of being lifted astride a pillow by Mose Walker in front of his saddle and allowed to ride on Old Lummox as he went about the ranch to perform his chores.

There was the first pony of his own that his father gave him. It was a sorrel mare named Old Minnie—a gentle enough animal except for one skittish trick. She would always rear on her haunches when Will first got into the saddle. The boy enjoyed this little thrill of excitement Old Minnie gave him, but his mother would cry out to his father, "Clem! Clem! Don't let him ride that horse. You'll get my boy killed."

"Don't worry, Mother," Will would grin down at her. "I can handle Old Minnie."

All his life the picture of his sweet-faced mother would be enshrined in his heart. She was always bustling around the house, which was usually filled with people. Everyone who passed the Rogers' ranch

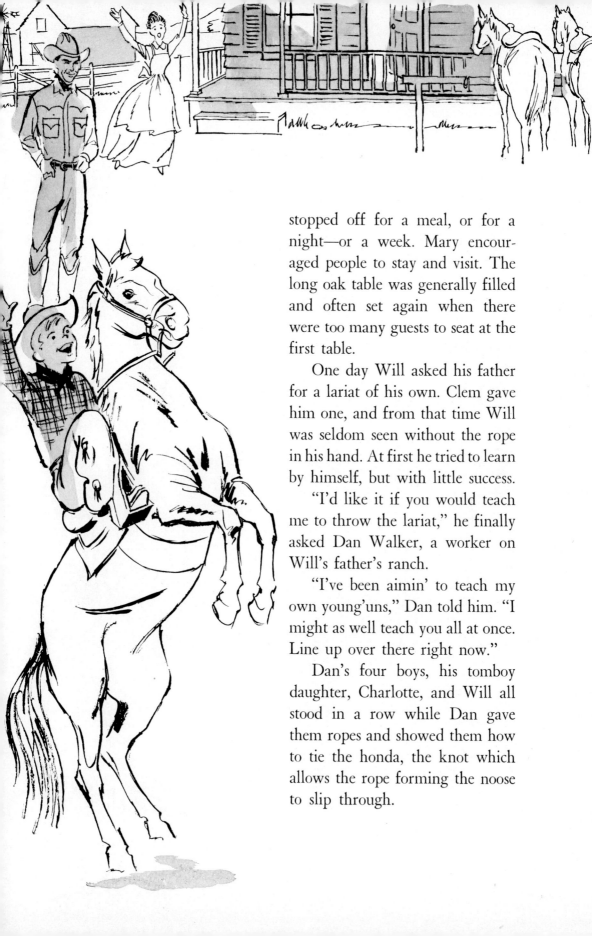

stopped off for a meal, or for a night—or a week. Mary encouraged people to stay and visit. The long oak table was generally filled and often set again when there were too many guests to seat at the first table.

One day Will asked his father for a lariat of his own. Clem gave him one, and from that time Will was seldom seen without the rope in his hand. At first he tried to learn by himself, but with little success.

"I'd like it if you would teach me to throw the lariat," he finally asked Dan Walker, a worker on Will's father's ranch.

"I've been aimin' to teach my own young'uns," Dan told him. "I might as well teach you all at once. Line up over there right now."

Dan's four boys, his tomboy daughter, Charlotte, and Will all stood in a row while Dan gave them ropes and showed them how to tie the honda, the knot which allows the rope forming the noose to slip through.

Will never tired of these lessons in lasso throwing, as the others often did; he begged for them every day. He was delighted to find that he had a natural knack and did much better than Dan's own children.

"If I don't look out, you all will beat me at this," Dan said one day. "Then you all can give me lessons. I never in my born days did see anyone take to ropin' the way you do."

Will only gave Dan his shy, crooked grin and practiced harder than ever.

One afternoon Will's oldest sister, Maude, was sent to the swimming hole to fetch him home to supper. They were crossing a pasture. Will turned to wave to his father approaching on horseback from the opposite direction.

"Run! Run!" his father shouted.

He heard Maude scream as she jerked his hand. Will, though, had a stubborn streak when ordered to do something and he often felt impelled to do just the opposite. He stood still and would not go with Maude. Finally she dropped his hand and ran. His father gal-

loped up and seized him under the arms and pulled him onto the
horse just in time to save him from the horns of an enraged bull.

As soon as they got to the barnyard, Will was yanked from the
horse and given one of the few thrashings he ever received. His
mother, hearing his yells, ran from the house and threw herself at
her husband.

"Clem! Stop it!" she cried. "You're hurting Willie."

Even when Clem told her the reason for the punishment, she protested that he was only a boy.

"Yes, but a rotten spoiled one," Clem growled. "He's got to learn
to mind. You're right, Mary. It's time he went to school."

There was one good thing about going away to school. It made
coming home seem so wonderful. The first thing he did was to race
for the pasture with rope and bridle in hand, to clamber on Comanche's bare back and gallop around the ranch, swinging his rope
and yelling "Yipee!" at the top of his voice. He threw his lariat at

calves, at goats, at chickens, and at the hired men, shouting with sat-
isfaction that he had not lost his skill. In fact, he was delirious with
joy over everything. His gray hound dog, Jim, followed, barking,
dashing ahead, turning himself almost inside out with delight at having his master back.

Will was so happy to be home that his father's severe lecture upon
his poor scholastic record bothered him not at all.

The morning after Will's return from school at Tahlequah, Mr.
Rogers said at breakfast, "I haven't time to take care of those dogie
calves. Unless they are raised by hand, a lot of them will die. If you
want to round them up and take over the responsibility of their care,
you can have them."

Will sat up straight, his eyes bright. "You mean I can have them
for my own?"

"For your own," Mr. Rogers replied. "But of course their entire
care will be yours, too. It's quite a job to raise orphan calves."

"Yipee!" Will cried, leaping from his chair, his breakfast forgotten. "That's the sort of job I hanker for. My own calves! Now I'm
really a cowboy."

WILL ROGERS: IMMORTAL COWBOY

He saddled Comanche and immediately got to work rounding up the dogies on the Rogers' range. He thought it was mighty fine of his father, whom he called the Chief, to give him the calves for his very own. He would see to it that they became the finest beef cattle in the county.

Every morning he set out early to comb the range for the orphans and nearly every day he returned with a dogie across Comanche's withers. All his calves were kept in a special corral, and at the end of the summer he had a herd of seventy-five. And what a struggle it was to keep them alive! The first step was to teach them to drink milk from a bucket. Will would hold the bucket in one hand, straddle the neck of a calf, and force its nose down into the milk. After much struggling and tussling, the dogie learned to drink. Later he drove them into one of the pastures and told them that now they were expected to eat grass like grown-up cows. He shoved their noses down into the new, tender grass as an example of what they were expected to do, but they snorted and struggled as they had when he first tried to make them drink milk. Finally he turned the family milk cow into the pasture.

"You teach those stubborn critters how to graze," he told her.

His scheme evidently worked, for when he returned in the evening most of his herd were either cropping the grass or lying down looking full and contented.

Will invited the Chief out to see how well his dogies were doing.

When his father said, "You've done all right," Will knew he was proud.

"You're a born cowman," Clem went on. "It won't be long until your herd can be turned out on the range, so we'll have to figure out a brand for you."

"Gosh!" Will exclaimed. "Am I going to have my own brand?"

"Certainly," his father replied. "Figure out one that will be easy to read."

They walked toward the house. Will's mind was busy trying to devise a unique brand for his calves.

"That's it!" he cried when they sat down in the living room.

He pointed to the andirons supporting the logs in the fireplace. "Mine will be the dog-iron brand."

"It's a good one," his father agreed, eyeing the circle supported by two straight legs.

Will felt that he had indeed become every inch a cowboy when he was allowed to rope and dab the branding iron on the rumps of his own calves. They were turned out on the range, but every day Will rode out to see how they were doing.

There was a new family on the ranch, living in one of the cabins. The mother, Mary Bible, kept house for the Rogers. She had several boys who were good companions for Will. Also, there was Bright Drake, from a neighboring ranch, who came over nearly every day, and the Barker and Dawson boys, and one boy in particular, Charley McClellan, who became Will's chum. Like Will, he was one-eighth Cherokee and very proud of his Indian blood. He wore a breechclout and moccasins, braided his long black hair, and liked to sleep out-of-doors on the ground, wrapped in a blanket.

Will helped drive herds of beef cattle to the railroad. He arose before sunup, gulped a hasty breakfast, then, on Comanche, trailed the herd. It was a wearying job which took two full days, but Will loved every minute of it.

He still practiced roping and once the prize turkey of a neighbor proved so tempting that his lariat whirled out in perfect aim and broke the fowl's long neck.

Feeling sorry, Will went into the house to apologize to the woman. "I aim to pay you for the bird," he said, twisting his hat in his hand.

"You shouldn't do things like that, Willie," the neighbor scolded. But when she saw the expression on his face she relented and went

on, "But never mind. I know it was an accident. I'll cook the turkey for dinner tomorrow and you can come and help eat it."

Will went, and took with him a fine new carving set for the neighbor.

Will Rogers attended a number of schools. He disliked them, and called them "prison walls." He gained one thing from attending school at Tahlequah—the discovery of his gift for making people laugh. The laughter had hurt at first, until he learned to play up to it. Now more and more of his friends expected him to be funny. He had a way of doing and saying things which opened people's hearts and his own, too. His friends' approval was like warm sun on growing things. His personality expanded and developed.

When he entered Willie Halsell College he was awkward, ill at ease, and painfully unsure of himself. At the end of his three years there, despite his poor scholastic record, he came out with the bent of his nature fully determined. His inimitable "gift of gab" had become part of him.

Will's next school was Scarritt College, at Neosho, Missouri. His classmates at Scarritt called him the Wild Indian.

"I'm glad I'm an Injun," he told them. "I feel sorry for anyone who doesn't have some Cherokee blood. Seems as how they aren't quite human."

As might be expected, the trunk which he took to Neosho was well loaded with lariats. One afternoon a mare belonging to the head-master strayed into the schoolyard, followed by its skittish colt. Will could never resist an interesting target, so his rope flew out and settled over the colt's neck. Snorting and nickering with terror, the colt, trying to escape, wound the rope around the mare's legs. In the mix-up Will lost hold of the rope and the mare and colt streaked across the tennis court, tearing down the net and fence and generally wrecking the place.

Will was summoned to the headmaster's office and told to pack his things and go home.

For a time Will worked hard on his father's ranch. Then the love of travel which always overtook him in the spring was too strong to resist. He became a wandering cowboy taking part in roping contests and rodeos.

WILL ROGERS: IMMORTAL COWBOY

Several years later, Will's father asked him to manage his ranch. Will fumbled for words. "Of course, I love the place," he said, twirling his rope and chewing gum. "I'll go to the ranch until the beef stock is ready to ship. But I'm not promising to stay. I've somehow got show business into my head."

Will Rogers loved to talk and to act. He became known as the "Cowboy Philosopher" and wrote on many subjects. Eventually he became a big attraction in moving pictures. Audiences loved him and money seemed to flow into his bank account. It flowed out in an amazing way, too. No one knows the number of friends, relatives, and charities he helped to support.

When he was praised, Will would say, "Aw shucks! I'm just a cowboy at heart—a cowboy that's had lots of luck."

During his most successful years he and his wife, Betty, built a "dream house" overlooking Santa Monica Bay, in California. Will and others called it the "House That Jokes Built."

His syndicated newspaper writings were famous, and he became a power in forming public opinion. Friends wanted him to go into

politics, but he grinned, saying, "If folks ever begin to take me seriously, I'm sunk." When offered an honorary degree by a noted university he said, "I'll stick to my degree of D.A.—Doctor of Applesauce."

Oklahoma, Colorado, and California all have memorials for Will Rogers. The Oklahoma memorial is built on a hill overlooking Claremore. When Rogers bought the hill he said, "I'll be coming back here someday when I'm old and the world is tired of my act. I'll build a home here on this hill and sit here and whittle and gab with my friends until the big Boss stages the last roundup and us strays head for the home corral." Will Rogers was fifty-six years old when he lost his life with his friend, Wiley Post, in an airplane crash in Alaska. He did not have a chance to build his home at Claremore but the ranch style memorial built by Oklahoma is much like the house he had planned as his last home.

Adaptation from *Will Rogers: Immortal Cowboy,* by Shannon Garst, by permission of Julian Messner, Inc.; copyright © 1950 by Dorris Shannon Garst.

Albert Schweitzer, Jungle Doctor

By May McNeer

THE old Lutheran church looked very high to a small boy sitting quietly in a dim pew, waiting for his father, Pastor Schweitzer, to come to the pulpit to preach. All around him Sunday garments rustled, yet if he moved so much as a finger his mother put a firm hand on his arm. Albert fixed his eyes intently on the organ. Would the Devil appear today? Suddenly there it was —a bearded face above the organ. Albert stiffened with fright, for who could it be but the Devil himself? The wonderful organ music swelled and grew until it filled the church with heavenly sounds. Albert forgot the Devil face. He felt almost faint with the music.

As he grew older, Albert came to know that the strange bearded face was not the Devil, but was a mirrored reflection of the organist, kindly Father Iltis. But his feeling about organ music never changed.

Albert, who was one of five children, was born in 1875 in Alsace-Lorraine. His home was the pleasant village of Günsbach, in a lovely rolling farm country. His was a happy childhood in a family that shared the same interests, and loved music and the church.

ALBERT SCHWEITZER, JUNGLE DOCTOR

He did not like to seem different, and insisted on wearing clothes like those of the peasant boys instead of the more dignified clothes of the parson's son. Although he liked his friends and wanted to be with them, he found it difficult sometimes to enter into their sports. One day in early spring he went out into the fields with a friend to hunt birds with a slingshot. As they walked along, Albert was hoping that they would not find any birds. Suddenly his companion whispered, "Look, a whole flock!" Albert, quivering all over at the thought of killing any creature, held his sling off balance so that he would miss.

As he stood there, watching his friend aim his stone carefully at the little birds picking at the grain, Albert heard church bells ringing sweetly over the fields. To him they seemed to say, "Thou shalt not

kill!" Albert threw down his slingshot and shouted loudly to frighten the birds away. As they whirred up into the safety of the blue sky and disappeared, he knew that he no longer cared if his friends made fun of him. He knew that he could not kill any living thing as a sport; that he would never kill except as a matter of absolute necessity.

Albert's interest in music grew rapidly. He tried to play the piano at home, and he listened happily to the singing of groups who enjoyed the folk songs of the region. When he was old enough, he entered the Lycee school in Mulhouse and went to live with his Uncle Louis and Aunt Sophie, who had no children. Uncle Louis was director of the school. Albert lived in Mulhouse eight years. At first he had trouble learning to be a good student, but his musical skill developed so fast that his teacher was astonished. At fifteen Albert was permitted to play the church organ. Later he entered the University of Strasbourg to take up religious studies, for he had decided to become a pastor.

When Albert Schweitzer was twenty-one years old he decided to devote the next ten years to religious studies and to music and, after that, to work for the rest of his life to relieve the suffering of others.

Schweitzer was a large man, of great energy, both mentally and physically. He began to plan his hours of work, his studies, writing, teaching, and music. He made a special study of Johann Sebastian Bach's music, and it was not long before he was recognized as a distinguished Bach authority, as well as a talented performer of Bach's music. Then he became widely known as a scholar. He lived in Paris for a time and studied music there. His publications attracted wide attention.

When Schweitzer was thirty-one, and was already distinguished in the fields of theology and music, he quietly entered a medical school to prepare himself to be a doctor. He decided to devote his life to the people in the jungles of Africa.

ALBERT SCHWEITZER, JUNGLE DOCTOR

In 1913, the doctor and his wife sailed for Africa, along with baggage that was mostly made up of medical supplies. Albert Schweitzer and his wife traveled from the coast up a strange river, winding through mysterious forests. In the water, herds of rhinoceroses wallowed, and crocodiles, thrusting their snouts out of the mud, looked like knotty floating logs. On shore, there were wild elephants that sometimes trampled native villages to ruins, and at night the darkness was pierced with the cry of lion or jackal. Here, a mile from the mission church by river canoe, the Schweitzers built their rough hospital. At first it was one shack, and then it grew as the doctor

labored day after day with his hands. He gradually gathered natives to help, and after a while he became a man who could lead and direct others, as well as a scholar and musician.

In the next few years the hospital became a small village. Natives heard of it and traveled great distances to be treated. With each new patient there came a whole family to camp in the clearing. The doctor had to give food to them all, and so he had the women cook for their sick relatives and bring food to their beds.

Doctor Schweitzer seemed to be everywhere at once, directing, healing, and working with his hands. He imported a herd of goats to supply milk. The goats climbed up on the roofs of the hospital huts and scrambled about as if they were on their native mountain peaks. There were other strange problems. A goat on the roof was not as bad as an elephant in a banana grove, breaking down delicate trees. There were mosquitoes to be fought, and the disease malaria, carried by mosquitoes, was always with them.

The Negroes of this region had little food and, until the hospital came, no medical treatment. They spoke many different tribal languages and believed in strange superstitions. The doctor took care of them all, with the help of medical men and nurses who came to give their time and energy.

The jungle doctor made several long trips back to Europe. During World War I he was held in prisons in France. Yet he always was sure that he would return to his work in Africa. At the end of World War II, a great interest in Doctor Schweitzer's work began to spread throughout the world. Money came in from America to make it possible to extend the hospital work. The doctor built a separate village for patients who had leprosy, away from the other hospital. Young doctors and nurses came to help, and the hospital received new equipment.

Honors were pouring in on the great doctor as he grew older. He was given the Nobel peace prize, and his music was put on records. His books became well known to scholars in colleges throughout the world.

The jungle doctor is a kindly man, but he can enforce his hospital rules sternly for the good of all. Like many others who have given a lifetime of service without a thought of reward, Doctor Schweitzer has received the only reward that means anything to him. This reward is the knowledge that he has been of service to those who need him. He has truly dedicated his talents and his labors to "reverence for life."

MYTHS AND LEGENDS

Pandora's Box

By Nathaniel Hawthorne

LONG, long ago, when this old world was young, there was a child named Epimetheus. He had neither father nor mother; and, that he might not be lonely, another child—who, like himself, had no father or mother —was sent from a far country to live with him and be his playmate. Her name was Pandora.

The first thing that Pandora saw when she entered the cottage where Epimetheus lived, was a great box. And almost the first question she asked was: "Epimetheus, what have you in that box?"

"My dear little Pandora," answered Epimetheus, "that is a secret, and you must not ask any questions about it. The box was left here to be kept safely, and I myself do not know what it contains."

It is thousands of years since Epimetheus and Pandora were alive. Then, everybody was a child. The children needed no fathers and mothers to take care of them, because there was no danger, no trouble of any kind. There were no clothes to be mended; and there was always plenty to eat and drink. Whenever a child wanted his dinner, he found it growing on a tree.

Most wonderful of all, the children never quarreled or cried. Those ugly little winged monsters, called Troubles, had never yet been seen on the earth. Probably the greatest hardship which a child had ever experienced was Pandora's vexation at not being able to discover the secret of the mysterious box. At first this was only the faint shadow of a Trouble; but every day it grew bigger.

"Whence can the box have come?" Pandora kept saying. "And what in the world can be inside of it?"

"Always talking about this box!" said Epimetheus. "I wish, dear Pandora, you would talk of something else. Come, let us go and gather some ripe figs, and eat them for our supper under the trees. I know a vine that has the sweetest and juiciest grapes you ever tasted."

"Always talking about grapes and figs!" cried Pandora, pettishly.

"Well, then," said Epimetheus, "let us run out and have a merry time with our playmates."

"I am tired of merry times," answered Pandora. "This ugly box! I think about it all the time, and I insist you tell me what is in it."

"As I have said, fifty times over, I do not know!" replied Epimetheus, a little vexed.

"You might open it," said Pandora, looking sideways at Epimetheus.

Epimetheus seemed so shocked at the idea of looking that Pandora thought it best not to suggest it any more. "At least," she said, "you can tell me how it came here."

"It was left at the door," replied Epimetheus, "just before you came, by a person who looked very smiling and intelligent. He could hardly keep from laughing as he put it down. He was dressed in an odd kind of a cloak, and had on a cap that seemed to be made partly of feathers, so that it looked almost as if it had wings."

"What sort of a staff had he?" asked Pandora.

"Oh, the most curious staff you ever saw!" cried Epimetheus. "It was like two serpents twisting around a stick, and was carved so naturally that, at first, I thought the serpents were alive."

"I know him," said Pandora thoughtfully. "It was Quicksilver. Nobody else has such a staff. He brought me hither, as well as the box. No doubt he intended it for me. It probably contains pretty dresses for me to wear, or toys for you and me to play with."

"Perhaps so," answered Epimetheus, turning away. "But until Quicksilver comes back and tells us so, we have neither of us any right to lift the lid of the box."

For the first time since her arrival, Epimetheus went out without asking Pandora to go with him. Pandora stood gazing at the box. Although she had called it ugly, it was a very handsome article of furniture. It was made of a beautiful kind of wood which was so highly polished that Pandora could see her face in it.

The edges and corners of the box were carved with wonderful skill. Around the margin there were figures of graceful men and women, and pretty children reclining or playing amid a profusion of flowers and foliage. These were all so exquisitely represented that they seemed to combine into a wreath of mingled beauty. But here and there, peeping forth from behind the carved foliage, Pandora fancied once or twice that she saw a face not so lovely. On looking more closely, however, and touching the spot with her finger, she could discover nothing of the kind. The most beautiful face of all was in the center of the lid. The features wore a lively and rather mischievous expression.

The box was fastened by a very complicated knot of gold cord. Never was a knot so cunningly twisted, with so many ins and outs that they defied the most skillful fingers to untangle them. Yet the very difficulty tempted Pandora to examine the knot.

"I believe that I begin to see how it was done," she said to herself. "Perhaps I could tie it up again, after undoing it. There would be no harm in that, surely. I need not open the box."

First, however, she tried to lift it. It was heavy; quite too heavy for the slender strength of a child. She raised one end of the box a few inches from the floor, and let it fall again, with a loud thump. A moment afterwards, she thought she heard something stir inside of the box. She put her ear as close as possible and listened. There did seem to be a kind of stifled murmur within! Or was it merely the singing in Pandora's ears? Her curiosity was stronger than ever.

She took the golden knot in her fingers and, without quite intending it, was soon busily engaged in trying to undo it. Meanwhile, the bright sunshine came through the open window. She stopped to listen as she heard the merry voices of the children playing at a distance. What a beautiful day it was!

All this time, however, her fingers were busy with the knot. When she happened to glance at the flower-wreathed face on the lid of the enchanted box, it seemed to be grinning at her.

"That face looks very mischievous," thought Pandora. "I wonder whether it smiles because I am doing wrong! I have the greatest mind in the world to run away!"

But just then, she gave the knot a kind of twist. The gold cord untwined itself as if by magic, and left the box without a fastening.

"This is the strangest thing I ever knew!" said Pandora. "What will Epimetheus say? And how can I possibly tie it up again?"

She made one or two attempts to restore the knot, but found it quite beyond her skill. It had disentangled itself so suddenly that she could not remember how the strings had been doubled into one another.

"When Epimetheus finds the knot untied, he will know that I

have done it," said Pandora. "How shall I make him believe that I have not looked into the box?"

And then the thought came into her naughty little heart that, since she would be suspected of having looked into the box, she might just as well do so at once. The enchanted face on the lid of the box seemed to smile at her, and she thought she heard, more distinctly than before, the murmur of small voices within.

"What can it be?" thought Pandora. "Is there something alive in the box? There cannot possibly be any harm in just one little peep!"

A great black cloud had been gathering in the sky, for some time past. Just as Epimetheus reached the cottage door, this cloud began to intercept the sunshine. He entered softly. Pandora had put her hand to the lid, and was on the point of opening the mysterious box.

Epimetheus himself was just as curious as Pandora. And if

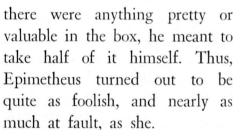

there were anything pretty or valuable in the box, he meant to take half of it himself. Thus, Epimetheus turned out to be quite as foolish, and nearly as much at fault, as she.

As Pandora raised the lid, the cottage grew very dark, for the black cloud had now swept over the sun. Pandora lifted the lid and looked inside. It seemed as if a sudden swarm of winged creatures brushed past her, as they flew out of the box.

At the same instant, she heard Epimetheus cry out as if in pain.

PANDORA'S BOX

Pandora let fall the lid. The thunder cloud had so darkened the room that she could scarcely see. But she heard a disagreeable buzzing. As her eyes grew accustomed to the dim light, she saw a crowd of ugly little shapes, with wings like bats, and armed with terrible, long stings in their tails. One of these had stung Epimetheus. Nor was it long before Pandora herself began to scream. An ugly little monster had settled on her forehead, and would have stung her if Epimetheus had not run and brushed it away.

Now these ugly things were the whole family of earthly Troubles. There were bad Tempers; there were a great many kinds of Cares; there were more than a hundred and fifty Sorrows; there were more kinds of Naughtiness than it would be of any use to talk about. In short, all the sorrows and worries that have since troubled mankind had been shut up in the mysterious box. It had been given to Epimetheus and Pandora to be kept safely. Had they been faithful to their trust, all would have gone well. No grown person would ever have been sad, and no child would have had cause to shed a single tear, from that hour until this moment. It was impossible for the two children to keep the ugly swarm in their own little cottage. The first thing they did was to fling open the doors and windows, in hopes of getting rid of them. And, sure enough, away flew the winged Troubles and so pestered and tormented the small people everywhere about that none of them so much as smiled for many days afterwards.

Meanwhile, the naughty Pandora and hardly less naughty Epimetheus remained in their cottage. Both of them had been grievously stung. Pandora flung herself upon the floor and rested her head on the box, sobbing as if her heart would break.

Suddenly there was a gentle tap on the inside of the lid.

"Who are you?" asked Pandora, with a little of her former curiosity. "Who are you, inside of this naughty box?"

A sweet voice spoke from within:

"Only lift the lid, and you shall see."

"No, no," answered Pandora, again beginning to sob, "I have had enough of lifting the lid! There are plenty of your ugly brothers and sisters already flying about the world. You need never think that I shall be so foolish as to let you out!"

"Ah," said the sweet voice again, "I am not like those naughty creatures that have stings in their tails. They are no brothers and sisters of mine, as you will see, if you will only let me out!"

There was a kind of cheerful witchery in the tone that made it almost impossible to refuse anything which this little voice asked. Pandora's heart had grown lighter at every word.

"My dear Epimetheus," cried Pandora, "shall I lift the lid again?"

"Just as you please," said Epimetheus. "You have done so much mischief already, that perhaps you may as well do a little more. One other Trouble can make no very great difference."

"You might speak a little more kindly!" murmured Pandora.

"Ah, naughty boy!" cried the little voice within the box, in an arch and laughing tone. "He knows he is longing to see me. Come, my dear Pandora, lift the lid. I am in a great hurry to comfort you."

"Epimetheus," exclaimed Pandora, "come what may, I am resolved to open the box!"

"As the lid seems very heavy," cried Epimetheus, running

across the room, "I will help you!"

With one consent, the two children lifted the lid. Out flew a sunny, fairylike creature, and hovered about the room, throwing a light wherever she went.

"Pray, who are you, beautiful creature?" asked Pandora.

"I am to be called Hope!" answered the sunshiny figure. "I was packed into the box that I might comfort people when that swarm of ugly Troubles was let loose among them."

"Your wings are colored like the rainbow!" exclaimed Pandora. "How very beautiful!"

"Yes, they are like the rainbow," said Hope, "because, glad as my nature is, I am made partly of tears as well as smiles."

"And will you stay with us," asked Epimetheus, "forever and ever?"

"As long as you live," said Hope. "There may come times when you will think that I have vanished. But again, and again, and again, when perhaps you least dream of it, you shall see the glimmer of my wings on the ceiling of your cottage."

Adapted from *The Paradise of Children*

The Flight of Icarus

Retold by ·Sally Benson

ONCE long ago in Greece there lived a famous mechanic named Daedalus. While visiting Crete, King Minos, the ruler of the island, became angry with him, and ordered him shut up in a high tower that faced the lonely sea. In time, with the help of his young son, Icarus, Daedalus managed to escape from the tower, only to find himself a prisoner on the island. Several times he tried by bribery to stow away on one of the vessels sailing from Crete, but King Minos kept strict watch over them and no ships were allowed to sail without being carefully searched.

Daedalus was an ingenious artist and was not discouraged by his failures. "Minos may control the land and sea," he said, "but he does not control the air. I will try that way."

He called his son Icarus to him and told the boy to gather up all the feathers he could find on the rocky shore. As thousands of gulls soared over the island, Icarus soon collected a huge pile of feathers. Daedalus then melted some wax and made a skeleton in the shape of a bird's wing. The smallest feathers he pressed into the soft wax, and the large ones he tied on with thread. Icarus played about on the beach happily while his father worked, chasing the feathers that blew away in the strong wind that swept the island.

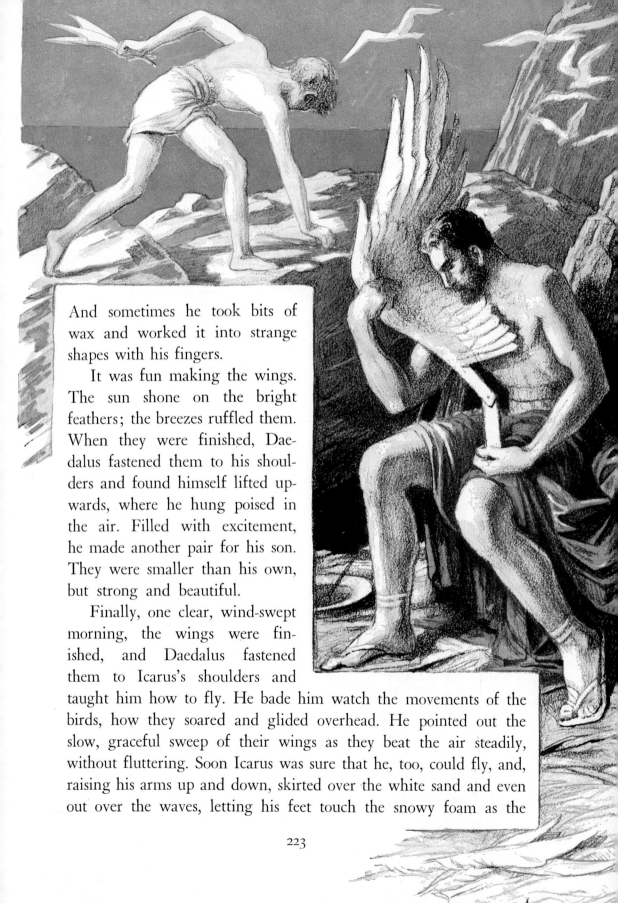

And sometimes he took bits of wax and worked it into strange shapes with his fingers.

It was fun making the wings. The sun shone on the bright feathers; the breezes ruffled them. When they were finished, Daedalus fastened them to his shoulders and found himself lifted upwards, where he hung poised in the air. Filled with excitement, he made another pair for his son. They were smaller than his own, but strong and beautiful.

Finally, one clear, wind-swept morning, the wings were finished, and Daedalus fastened them to Icarus's shoulders and taught him how to fly. He bade him watch the movements of the birds, how they soared and glided overhead. He pointed out the slow, graceful sweep of their wings as they beat the air steadily, without fluttering. Soon Icarus was sure that he, too, could fly, and, raising his arms up and down, skirted over the white sand and even out over the waves, letting his feet touch the snowy foam as the

223

water thundered and broke over the sharp rocks.

Daedalus watched him proudly but with misgivings. He called Icarus to his side, and putting his arm around the boy's shoulders, said, "Icarus, my son, we are about to make our flight. No human being has ever traveled through the air before, and I want you to listen carefully to my instructions. Keep at a moderate height, for if you fly too low the fog and spray will clog your wings, and if you fly too high the heat will melt the wax that holds them together. Keep near me and you will be safe."

He kissed Icarus and fastened the wings more securely to his son's shoulders. Icarus, standing in the bright sun, the shining wings drooping gracefully from his shoulders, his golden hair wet with spray and his eyes bright and dark with excitement, looked like a lovely bird. Daedalus's eyes filled with tears and, turning away, he soared into the sky and called to Icarus to follow. From time to time, he looked back to see that the boy was safe and to note how he managed his wings in his flight. As they flew across the land to test their prowess before setting out across the dark wild sea, ploughmen below stopped their work and shepherds gazed in wonder, thinking Daedalus and Icarus were gods.

W.T. BENDA

THE FLIGHT OF ICARUS

Father and son flew over Samos and Delos which lay to their left, and Lebinthus, which lay on their right. Icarus, beating his wings in joy, felt the thrill of the cool wind on his face and the clear air above and below him. He flew higher and higher up into the blue sky until he reached the clouds. His father saw him and called out in alarm. He tried to follow him, but he was heavier and his wings would not carry him.

Up and up Icarus soared, through the soft, moist clouds and out again toward the glorious sun. He was bewitched by a sense of freedom and beat his wings frantically, so that they would carry him higher and higher to heaven itself. The blazing sun beat down on the wings and softened the wax. Small feathers fell from the wings and floated softly down, warning Icarus to stay his flight and glide to earth. But the enchanted boy did not notice them until the sun became so hot that the largest feathers dropped off and he began to sink. Frantically he fluttered his arms, but no feathers remained to hold the air. He cried out to his father, but his voice was submerged in the blue waters of the sea, which has forever after been called by his name.

Daedalus, crazed by anxiety, called back to him, "Icarus! Icarus, my son, where are you?" At last he saw the feathers floating from the sky and soon his son plunged through the clouds into the sea. Daedalus hurried to save him, but it was too late. He gathered the boy in his arms and flew to land, the tips of his wings dragging in the water from the double burden they bore. Weeping bitterly, he buried his small son and called the land Icaria in his memory.

Then, with a flutter of wings, he once more took to the air, but the joy of his flight was gone and his victory over the air was bitter to him. He arrived safely in Sicily, where he built a temple to Apollo and hung up his wings as an offering to the god.

From *Gods and Heroes*

Midas and the Golden Touch

Retold by KATHERINE PYLE

A CERTAIN king named Midas was once so fortunate as to oblige the young god Dionysius. Dionysius, in return, bade Midas ask for anything he wished, and promised that whatever it was, it should be his.

Now Midas was a miser, loving gold more than anything else in all the world. Filled with joy, he cried out in his greed, "O Dionysius, if this is the truth—if thou wilt truly grant whatever thing I wish—let everything I touch turn into gold!"

The god laughed. "A most foolish wish, O thou most foolish king!" he cried. "Choose anything but that! I warn thee that the Golden Touch will only bring thee misery!"

But Midas clamored all the louder, "Nay, the Golden Touch! 'Tis all I ask!"

"Then it is thine!" said Dionysius, and lightly he laid his finger for a moment on the forehead of the king.

At once Midas felt a cold and heavy weight upon his limbs, and looking down he saw his garments all turned to gold. He touched a near-by branch (for he and his attendants had met Dionysius in the

MIDAS AND THE GOLDEN TOUCH

wood), and it was golden, too. He lifted a clod of earth, and in his hand it turned to solid gold.

Hardly able to believe in his good fortune, Midas thanked the god and hurried away. He was eager to try his gift at home, and turn his palace into gold—his garden and his trees and everything he owned.

As he passed through his palace gates he touched the pillars on either hand, and laughed to see the hue of gold sweep over them. His favorite hound came bounding out to meet him. Not thinking of what he did, Midas stooped to pat its head. Instantly the hound hardened into the leaping image of a dog, perfect in every line and curve and separate hair, but all of gold!

A moment Midas stood dismayed, then sighed, "It was my favorite hound; but what of that? What is one dog when weighed against a world of gold?"

So he passed on into the hall. Nor did he see how those about him drew aside, as though they feared that he might brush against them as he passed.

And now Midas called for food and wine, for he was hungry and thirsty. They were brought and set before him. Lost in a dream of all he meant to do, Midas took a piece of bread to break it, but in his hand it was a lump of gold. He seized an apple from a bowl. It was as golden as the far-famed fruit of the Hesperides. The meat he tried to eat hardened between his teeth into

tasteless metal.

With a loud cry of terror Midas started up. "O cruel Dionysius!" he cried. "Why should he grant a wish he knew could only destroy me! But he shall take it back! I will not keep the Golden Touch. Better to live in poverty than die of riches."

Gathering his golden robes about him, he set out in haste in search of Dionysius. His attendants followed him, but not too close.

He found the young god where he had left him, and throwing himself down before him cried, "Have pity on me, Dionysius! Free me from the Golden Touch before I die of thirst and hunger."

Then again Dionysius laughed. "Hast thou so soon then wearied of thy choice?" he cried. "I cannot take away the thing I gave; but go to the source of the River Pactolus. There bathe thy face and head and arms in the clear water at its fountainhead. It may wash away the Golden Touch. If not, then nothing can aid thee."

Then Midas sprang up and hastened to where the Pactolus flowed down from among its hills. He followed the stream up to its source, and there he knelt and plunged his hands into the stream, and shuddered as he saw how, at once, its sands and pebbles all were turned to gold. He laved his face and arms, and as he did so a sudden sense of lightness and of ease came over him.

Rising, he half fearfully touched a branch beside him, and saw with joy that it still was green. A bush near by was laden with berries, and he plucked and ate, and they were sweet and juicy in his mouth. He made a crown of leaves and placed it on his head; it still was freshly green.

So was Midas freed of the Golden Touch, and with it went all his greed for gold. He never returned again to his palace and his treasure rooms, but lived out in the fields and woods, a worshipper of Pan, and happy with the humble things of life, such as the poorest peasant might enjoy.　　　　From *Tales from Greek Mythology*

Persephone

By Flora J. Cooke

DEMETER had the care of all the plants, fruits, and grains in the world. She taught the people how to plow the fields and plant the seeds. She helped them gather in their harvests. They loved the kind Earth Mother and gladly obeyed her. They also loved her daughter, the beautiful Persephone.

Persephone wandered all day in the meadows among the flowers. Wherever she went, the birds, singing merrily, flocked after her.

The people said, "Where Persephone is, there is the warm sunshine. Flowers bloom when she smiles. Listen to her voice: it is like a bird's song."

Demeter wished always to have her child near her. But one day Persephone went alone into a meadow near the sea. She made a wreath of delicate blossoms for her hair, and gathered all the flowers that her apron could hold.

Far away across the meadow she saw a white flower gleaming. She ran to it and found it was a narcissus, but far more beautiful than any she had ever seen. On a single stem were a hundred blossoms. She tried to pick it, but the stem would not break. With all her strength she grasped it, and slowly the narcissus came up by the roots.

W. T. Benda

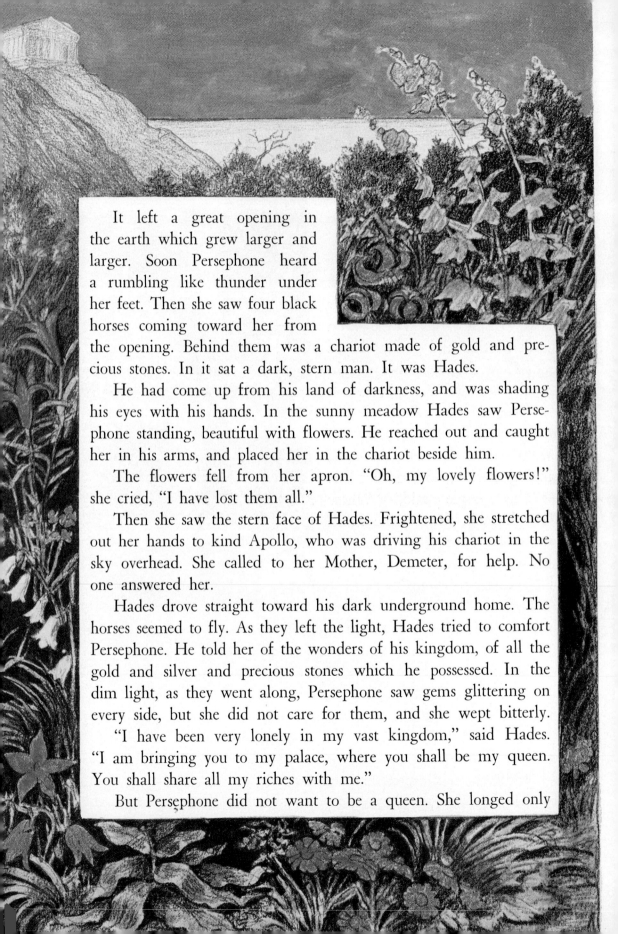

It left a great opening in the earth which grew larger and larger. Soon Persephone heard a rumbling like thunder under her feet. Then she saw four black horses coming toward her from the opening. Behind them was a chariot made of gold and precious stones. In it sat a dark, stern man. It was Hades.

He had come up from his land of darkness, and was shading his eyes with his hands. In the sunny meadow Hades saw Persephone standing, beautiful with flowers. He reached out and caught her in his arms, and placed her in the chariot beside him.

The flowers fell from her apron. "Oh, my lovely flowers!" she cried, "I have lost them all."

Then she saw the stern face of Hades. Frightened, she stretched out her hands to kind Apollo, who was driving his chariot in the sky overhead. She called to her Mother, Demeter, for help. No one answered her.

Hades drove straight toward his dark underground home. The horses seemed to fly. As they left the light, Hades tried to comfort Persephone. He told her of the wonders of his kingdom, of all the gold and silver and precious stones which he possessed. In the dim light, as they went along, Persephone saw gems glittering on every side, but she did not care for them, and she wept bitterly.

"I have been very lonely in my vast kingdom," said Hades. "I am bringing you to my palace, where you shall be my queen. You shall share all my riches with me."

But Persephone did not want to be a queen. She longed only

for her mother and the bright
sunshine and the sweet-smelling
meadows.

Soon they came to the palace
of Hades. It seemed very dark and
dismal to Persephone, and very
cold, too. A feast was ready for her, but she would not eat. She
knew that anyone who ate in Hades' home could never again return to earth. She was very unhappy, though Hades tried in many
ways to please her.

Everything on the earth was unhappy, too.

One by one the flowers hung their heads and said, "We cannot
bloom, for Persephone has gone."

The trees dropped their leaves and moaned, "Persephone has
gone, gone."

The birds flew away, calling, "We cannot sing, for Persephone
has gone."

Demeter was more miserable than anyone else. She had heard
Persephone call her, and had gone swiftly home to find her. She

searched all the earth for her child.

She asked everyone she met on her way these questions, "Have you seen Persephone? Where is Persephone?"

The only answer she ever received was, "Gone, gone. Persephone is gone!"

Soon Demeter became a wrinkled old woman. No one would have known that she was the kind mother who had always smiled on the people. She sat mourning day and night, her great tears falling steadily upon the cold ground. Nothing grew upon the earth and all became dreary and barren.

It was useless for the people to plow the soil. It was useless to plant the seeds. Nothing could grow without the help of Demeter, and all the people were idle and sad.

Demeter wandered into many lands, and when she found no one on earth who could tell her about Persephone, she looked up toward the sky. There she saw Apollo in his bright chariot. He was not driving as high in the sky as he was wont to do. He had been hidden by dark mists so that no one had been able to see him for many days.

Demeter knew that he must know about Persephone, for he could see all things on earth and in the sky.

"O great Apollo," she cried, "pity me, and tell me where my child is hidden."

Then Apollo told Demeter that Hades had carried Persephone away and that she was with him in his underground home.

Demeter hastened to great Father Zeus, who could do all things. She asked him to send to Hades for her daughter. Zeus called Hermes. He bade him go as swiftly as the wind to the home of Hades.

Hermes gladly obeyed, and he whispered the joyful news to all he met on his way. "I am going for Persephone. I am going for Persephone. Be ready to welcome her back!"

PERSEPHONE

He soon arrived in the gloomy kingdom under the earth. He gave Hades the message from Zeus. He told about the barren earth and of how Demeter was mourning for her child. He said she would not let anything grow until Persephone came back. "The people will starve if she does not soon return," he said.

Then Persephone wept bitterly, for that very day she had eaten a pomegranate and swallowed six of its seeds, and she remembered that whoever ate in Hades' home could never return to earth again.

But Hades took pity upon her and said, "Go, Persephone, back to the sunshine. But the law must be obeyed, and you shall come back every year to stay with me one month for each seed that you have eaten. That is all I ask."

Joy gave her wings, and as swiftly as Hermes himself, Persephone flew up into the sunshine.

Suddenly the flowers sprang up. The birds flocked together and sang; the trees put on bright green leaves. Everything, great and small, began to say in is own language, "Be happy, for Persephone has come! Persephone has come!"

Demeter was so benumbed with sorrow that she did not at once heed these voices. But soon she saw the great changes all about her and was puzzled. "Can the earth be ungrateful? Does it so soon forget my sweet Persephone?" she cried.

It was not long, however, before her own face grew radiant. She became once more the kind Earth Mother, for she held again her beloved child in her arms.

When Demeter found that Persephone could stay with her only half the year, she brought out the choicest treasures from the storehouse, and while Persephone stayed, the world was filled with beauty and joy.

When she had gone, Demeter carefully covered the rivers and lakes, and spread a soft white blanket over the sleeping earth.

From *Nature Myths and Stories*

Balder

By Flora J. Cooke

THE people in the North once believed that high above the clouds was the beautiful plain of Asgard. In it stood Valhalla, the vast feast hall of Odin, and all around it were the splendid golden and silver palaces of the other gods. And in the middle of the plain of Asgard, and apart from the other dwellings, was a pure-white palace. Only that which was fair and good ever dared to enter this palace, for it was the home of Balder, god of sunlight and gladness. Because of his great beauty and wisdom, he was called "Balder the beautiful" and "Balder the good."

Everything loved him. Joy filled the world when he smiled. The dull rocks and the gray old mountains softened with lichens and ferns the face which they turned to Balder. The birds waked at dawn to praise him. For him the bare trees burst into bloom, and there was nothing on earth too small or too sad to welcome him.

But one night Balder dreamed that he must soon leave Asgard and all the things which he so dearly loved. The next night he dreamed that he was living in the black, gloomy, underground world. The third night, when the same terrible dream came to him, he was greatly troubled and in the morning he told Odin,

his father, and Frigga, his mother, about it.

Odin, in alarm, called together his wisest gods and heroes. They only shook their heads and could do nothing to help him.

But Frigga cried, "It shall not be. I, his mother, will save him. I shall ask all things on earth to swear an oath not to harm Balder."

So Frigga sent her messengers into all parts of the world, and everything—fire, water, iron and all metals, stones, trees, diseases, beasts, birds, poisons, and all creeping things—gladly promised what she asked. They wondered at the question, for they thought, "Who could wish to hurt the gentle Balder?"

But Odin, Balder's father, was not satisfied with what Frigga had done, for he knew all things and his heart was very heavy. He feared that nothing could save Balder from death.

All the other gods, however, trusted in the great Frigga, and they rejoiced when they heard of the oath which all things had given her.

In their joy they found a new way to do Balder honor. He stood in their midst while the most skillful gods and heroes hurled their arrows at him. At first they threw only small twigs and stones. Everything, however, soon proved itself true to its promise. Then the heroes lost all fear of harming him, and amused themselves by throwing their huge swords, battle-axes, and other warlike weapons. But always Balder stood unharmed and smiling among them. For many days they gathered on the plains for this strange sport, and all things proved their love for Balder.

Loki, alone, was unhappy. Loki was the wicked one in Asgard. He was always doing clever, evil things against the gods. His schemes were usually unkind, and most of the misery in Asgard was caused by Loki's cruel tricks.

Now, when Loki saw that Balder was unharmed, he was vexed that nothing had been able to hurt him. He took the form of an old woman and went to Frigga's palace and asked her if she knew what the gods were doing. She answered that they were throwing darts and stones at Balder without being able to hurt him.

"Neither stones nor arrows, nor anything else can hurt Balder," said she, "for I have an oath from all of them."

"What!" said the old woman, "have all things sworn to spare Balder?"

"All," replied Frigga, "except one little shrub growing upon the eastern side of Valhalla, called the mistletoe. I thought that one too young and feeble to take the oath."

As soon as Loki heard this he took his own form again and soon found the mistletoe and cut it off. Then he went back to the place where the gods were gathered playing the game.

Soon Loki saw blind Hoder standing apart from the others— the only one in Asgard who could not join in the game. He was Balder's brother and loved him dearly. This was the chance the wicked Loki was looking for. He went straight to Hoder and said,

"Hoder, why dost thou not do Balder honor? Why dost thou not, too, throw something at him?"

"Because I am blind," Hoder answered. "And besides, I have nothing to throw."

"Here is my arrow," said Loki. "Take it and do thy best. I will guide thy arrow to the place where he stands."

Alas, the cruel Loki had made the arrow of mistletoe. He knew that this was the only way in which Balder could be harmed. He longed to see the surprise of the heroes when Balder should at last be wounded.

Hoder took the mistletoe, and, guided by Loki's hand, away flew the arrow. Balder the beautiful, pierced through and through, fell lifeless to the ground.

Then all Asgard was dark with sorrow. Strong heroes wept and would not be comforted. The earth grew cold and white and still. The water would not flow and the trees refused to grow. The birds became silent and no flowers breathed their fragrance into the air.

Odin said, "This is the doom that was foretold at his birth," and he bade the sorrowing gods build a funeral pyre worthy of Balder.

Then Hoder, pale with grief, begged that he might die and go himself to Hela's regions to take Balder's place. But his mother, Frigga, said that there was but one messenger, Hermod, the swiftest of the gods, who could go. Therefore she sent Hermod on Odin's horse to the spirit world to beg Queen Hela to release Balder.

And after three days Hermod returned saying, "Rejoice, for Hela says if everything living and lifeless weep for Balder, he may return to us."

And there was great happiness in Asgard that day. "Surely," they thought, "everything in the world will weep for Balder."

They had forgotten the cruel Loki.

Again Frigga sent messengers into all parts of the world, this time to ask for tears for Balder. And all went well until at length the messengers went beyond the edge of Asgard into a forest filled with iron trees. There, before a dark cavern, sat a shriveled hag, toothless and old, who gibed at them and said,

"Why come you here to my iron forest? Do you scorn heaven and wish a change?"

And they answered, "We come, not for gibes, but for tears."

They told her how Hela held Balder prisoner until all things on earth should weep for him. They begged her not to grudge her tears. But with a loud laugh the hag replied, "I weep him not. Let Hela keep him safe."

With a horrid grin, she fled, mocking, into the cavern's depth. Then they knew the old woman was no other than the wicked Loki.

But because there was one pair of dry eyes on the earth Balder could not return to Asgard.

Then all the gods hastened to obey Odin's command. For twelve days and nights they worked as only love can make men work. They did not pause for food or rest. They built a funeral pyre, and nothing was too small or too weak to help in the work of love.

238

They found Balder's ship upon the seashore and brought
great logs from the forest and
bound them upon the deck.
Upon these they placed his
beautiful white horse, his dogs,
his shining armor, and many
things which he loved upon earth.
And by his side they placed his
dear wife, Nanna, who had died
of grief. When all was finished,
they raised the sails, set the ship on fire, and pushed it out upon
the sea. They stood upon the seashore and wept all night until,
at sunrise, the sails fell into the dark water. They watched the
flames die down, and the waves wash over the sinking ship.

But the gods felt deep in their hearts that a time would come
when Balder would return.

From *Nature Myths and Stories*

The Story of King Arthur

By Eleanor Farjeon

WHEN King Uther Pendragon came to die, England was left once more without a ruler. All the Lords of the land wondered among themselves who would be the next King.

Now there was living at that time a wise enchanter called Merlin. He could see into the future as well as into the past; and he had been the friend of Uther Pendragon, and knew his wishes. So Merlin sent messages to all the Lords, saying that they must come to London by Christmas to meet together in St. Paul's.

When the Lords came, there in St. Paul's Churchyard they saw a great marble stone, and in the middle of it was stuck a sword. On the sword these words were written:

WHOEVER PULLS THIS SWORD OUT OF THIS STONE
IS THE TRUE KING OF ENGLAND

One after another the Lords tried to pull out the sword, but though many of them were great Princes and strong Knights,

not one could pull it out. They
ordered ten Knights to guard the
sword, and sent word through
the country that on New Year's
Day there would be a great tournament in
London, which all the Knights and Barons
in England must attend; and on that day
perhaps the true King would be found among them.

On New Year's Day all the roads to London and all the London streets were filled with old Knights and young, riding to the tournament in their shining armor; and with them rode their ladies in their fine dresses; and their prancing horses had embroidered cloths of scarlet and blue and gold on their backs.

Among the Knights rode old Sir Ector and his son Sir Kay. With them was Arthur, Sir Kay's young brother, a beautiful boy who was not yet old enough to be a knight.

Now on the way Sir Kay turned to Arthur and said, "Brother, what a fool I am! I have left my sword at home, and cannot fight in the tourney."

"I'll ride back and fetch it," said Arthur readily, and turned his horse's head, and galloped up the street. But when he got to Sir Ector's house it was locked, for all the people had gone to watch the tournament. So Arthur could not get in to fetch Kay's sword.

When he had knocked in vain on the door, he grew impatient, and said to himself, "I'll ride to St. Paul's Churchyard and take the sword out of the stone. Kay must not be without a sword this day."

So off he rode again, and the Churchyard was as empty as Sir Ector's house, for the ten Knights had also gone to the tournament. With a quick, light tug, Arthur pulled out the sword, and rode away with it to his brother.

As soon as Kay set eyes on it he knew what sword it was. He showed it to his father, saying, "Sir, here is the sword of the stone, so I must be King of the land."

Sir Ector was amazed, and when Kay had told all the story he called young Arthur, and the three returned to the Churchyard. There Sir Ector put the sword back into the stone and said,

"Now let us see! For only the true King of the land can pull it out."

So saying, he pulled himself at the sword, but it did not move. Then Kay pulled, and still the sword stuck fast.

"Now let Arthur try," said Sir Ector.

"I will," said Arthur, and pulled it out easily.

Then Sir Ector and Sir Kay knelt down before him.

"Alas!" said Arthur. "My own dear father and brother, why do you kneel to me?"

"My lord," said old Sir Ector, "it is time for you to know that I am not your father, and Kay is not your brother, except in love. Your true father was King Uther Pendragon himself. The night you were born the enchanter Merlin carried you away from the castle, and gave you to me to bring up in safety."

Then Arthur was sad at heart, for he had always thought of good Sir Ector as his father, and he could not all at once feel glad of his real father, though it was King Uther Pendragon himself. Nevertheless it was the truth, and Arthur knew he must now be King in his turn.

On Twelfth Day the Knights and the Barons came to the Churchyard, and none of them could move the sword in the stone. But Arthur pulled it out before them all. Then they were angry that so young a boy should do what they could not do, and prove himself their King; and they said,

"How do we know he is really the son of Uther Pendragon? Most likely it is a falsehood. Let us wait till Candlemas, and try again."

At Candlemas they came together and tried the sword again, and none but Arthur could move it. So the Barons said,

"Let us wait till Christmas!"

And at Christmas Arthur drew the sword again.

"Let us wait till Easter!" cried the Barons.

But at Easter none but Arthur could draw the sword, and the

Barons shouted,

"Let us wait till Pentecost!"

Now Merlin the Enchanter searched through England, and got together all the Knights who had been loved and trusted by King Uther Pendragon. These men gathered round young Arthur, and swore to serve and honor him, and when Pentecost came they rode with him to the Churchyard. There were all the Knights and Barons waiting, and there too were all the common people watching. And once more Arthur pulled the sword out of the stone, with the whole of London looking on.

Then all the People shouted, and cried out,

"We will have Arthur for our King, for it is the will of God! Whoever is against it, we will kill him!"

And the great crowd, rich and poor together, knelt down to young King Arthur.

Arthur laid the sword upon the altar in the church and was crowned King. And he swore to be a true King to the Lords and the People all the days of his life.

The People, rich and poor, then spoke to him of their sufferings since the death of Uther Pendragon. Some had lost their land, and some their money. In some parts of the land roamed strange and dangerous beasts. In other parts lived giants, who killed the men and imprisoned the lovely ladies. And Arthur said,

"I will clear the land of all these evils."

Whenever he heard a new tale of wrong, he went himself, or sent one of his Knights on the adventure, to make all right again.

In his castle in Camelot he had a round table built, and here he sat with all the best Knights in England around him. And the greatest honor any man could have in those days was to be one of Arthur's Knights of the Round Table.

From *Mighty Men*

The Story of William Tell

Retold by James Baldwin

THE PEOPLE of Switzerland were not always free and happy. Many years ago a proud tyrant, whose name was Gessler, ruled over them, and made their lot a bitter one indeed.

One day this tyrant set up a tall pole in the public square, and put his own cap on the top of it; and then he gave orders that every man who came into the town should bow down before it. But there was one man, named William Tell, who would not do this. He stood up straight with folded arms, and laughed at the swinging cap. He would not bow down to Gessler himself.

When Gessler heard of this, he was very angry. He was afraid that other men would disobey, and that soon the whole country would rebel against him. So he made up his mind to punish the bold man.

William Tell's home was among the mountains, and he was a famous hunter. No one in all the land could shoot with bow and arrow so well as he. Gessler knew this, and so he thought of a cruel plan to make the hunter's own skill bring him to grief. He ordered that Tell's little boy should be made to stand up in the public square with an apple on his head; and then he bade Tell shoot the apple with one of his arrows.

245

Tell begged the tyrant not to have him make this test of his skill. What if the boy should move? What if the bowman's hand should tremble? What if the arrow should not carry true?

"Will you make me kill my boy?" he said.

"Say no more," said Gessler. "You must hit the apple with your one arrow. If you fail, my soldiers shall kill the boy before your eyes."

Then, without another word, Tell fitted the arrow to his bow. He took aim, and let it fly. The boy stood firm and still. He was not afraid, for he had faith in his father's skill.

The arrow whistled through the air. It struck the apple fairly in the center, and carried it away. The people shouted with joy.

As Tell was turning away from the place, an arrow which he had hidden under his coat dropped to the ground.

"Fellow!" cried Gessler, "what mean you with this second arrow?"

"Tyrant!" was Tell's proud answer, "this arrow was for your heart if I had hurt my child."

And there is an old story that, not long after this, Tell did shoot the tyrant with one of his arrows; and thus he set his country free.

From *Fifty Famous Stories*

Robin Hood and Maid Marian

By George Cockburn Harvey

NOW, while Robin Hood was leading his men in Sherwood Forest and living the life of a bold outlaw, his thoughts were often full of someone whom he had left behind in his old home. This was Maid Marian, the beautiful daughter of a great man whose house had stood near Robin's home. Robin Hood and Maid Marian had been close friends since childhood. They had played together, hunting for birds' nests, fishing in the brook, climbing trees or running races over the meadow grass, and when Robin was forced to go out into the world he bore a sore heart with him after parting with Marian.

Since Robin's departure things had gone very hardly with Marian also. Her parents died, her friends proved unkind, and her heart often dwelt on the friend of her youth—bold, brave Robin. For a long time she did not know where he was, but at last his name began to ring through the North Countree, and she knew that her old friend had become the renowned outlaw of whose daring

deeds minstrels sang, and of whom men talked as they sat about the evening fire.

At last, lonely and friendless as she was, Maid Marian resolved to seek Robin in Sherwood Forest and see if he still remembered the old happy days of their childhood. She knew how unsafe it was for a woman to travel about the country alone, so she put on the dress of a page and took quiver and bow, sword and buckler. Thus armed and disguised, she set out to seek Robin. At last she reached the outskirts of the great forest, and as soon as she entered the dark shades of the mighty oaks she eagerly watched for the first sign of a forest dweller who could direct her to the haunts of her old friend.

As it happened, that very morning Robin had set out alone to make an expedition in search of news. He had taken great care to disguise himself, for the Sheriff of Nottingham had given orders that every outlaw should be put to death upon capture, and no mercy whatever should be shown.

So Robin went out in a ragged suit of hodden-gray (coarse, gray cloth), with a big hat down over his face, and a huge patch over his left eye, and a tattered cloak huddled over his shoulders. He had been walking an hour or more when he saw the figure of a handsomely dressed stripling coming along the way towards him. Robin at once stepped out of sight behind a bush until he could be sure that the youth was alone. In these days it behooved him to be wary, so many and so fierce were his enemies. He suspected some trap at the sight of every stranger. But the youth came on with a quick, even step, and seemed to be entirely alone. Just as he was passing the bush behind which Robin stood, the outlaw sprang out and commanded him to stand.

"Who art thou, and what dost thou want in Sherwood?" demanded Robin Hood.

The stranger was Maid Marian, and she looked at Robin and never dreamed that her old friend stood before her in the person of this wild, ragged man of the woods. She thought it was some savage free-booter who would belike plunder her, and she sprang back and laid her hand on her sword.

"This is not one of Robin's men," thought Maid Marian. "This is some footpad whom I must meet boldly or I am undone." So she said, "Stand aside, fellow, and let me go on my way. I have nought to do with thee."

"Ay, but I may have something to do with thee," replied the tattered stranger. "Tell me whither and why thou goest through the forest or I must turn thee back."

"Turn me back," said the page. "That wilt thou never do, rude man. Put me not to the need of drawing sword in my defense or thou mayst well rue the day."

"Why, this is a brave springald (youngster)!" laughed Robin Hood. "And what wouldst thou do with that pretty little bodkin of thine?"

"'Tis a bodkin that thou mayst find over sharp," said the page, and drew the glittering blade from its sheath, and waved it on high. "Give way, for I seek the heart of the forest and none shall check me."

When Robin heard that the newcomer was bound for the depths of Sherwood, his suspicions grew fast. It seemed to him that a bold, smart lad such as this was just the person the Sheriff might send as a spy, and he became resolved to turn the page back. "Nay," said Robin, "I bid you return. Seek your own safety and leave the forest glades in peace, or I shall be compelled to draw weapon also."

"Draw and I will draw!" cried the other. "But go back I will not."

"The sight of my blade will frighten a mere lad like this," thought Robin, and he drew out his sword and sprang forward and made a lunge as if in fierce attack. But, to his surprise, the lunge was deftly turned aside, and the slender page met him as boldly with sword and buckler as ever Robin had been met in his life.

Clash-clash! went their swords as the keen blades grated together. But Robin did not put out the whole of his strength and skill against a mere lad like this, and so the combat lasted much longer than it would otherwise have done. Nor was the page at all unskilled in sword play, for on one occasion Robin's guard was passed and he received a small wound in the face. The outlaw

became full of admiration for this brave young opponent and tried to make a peaceful ending to their fray.

"Hold thy hand," said Robin Hood, "and thou shalt range the forest with bold Robin Hood and hear the sweet song of the nightingale."

"What!" screamed the page. "Robin Hood! And are you indeed Robin Hood? And oh, Robin, I have hurt you! I knew you not, Robin."

The outlaw started in surprise at the figure before him.

"Why, who art thou?" he said. "And why should it trouble thee that I am hurt?"

"I came hither to seek you, Robin," cried the page, "but never dreamed that I should meet you in this guise. And, Robin, don't you know me?"

Robin Hood stood for a few moments in greater wonder still at the fair, blushing face; then memory rose like a flood.

"I know you!" he cried. "I know you now! You are Maid Marian. Dearest Marian, how came you here?"

"I came to seek you, Robin," she replied, "for I have no friend in the world but you. And I knew you not and have wounded you."

"Tush! That is nothing," said Robin. "We get many shrewder cuts and knocks in the greenwood. And as for not knowing me, that is no wonder. I am disguised lest my enemy, the Sheriff of Nottingham, should seize me."

The two friends now sat down on a mossy bank near at hand and fell into talk, telling each other how their lives had passed since their separation. "And have you room for me in the greenwood, Robin?" asked Maid Marian.

"Ay, and proud to see you there, Marian," cried the outlaw. And so Maid Marian came to Sherwood and reigned as queen of the forest revels.

From *Robin Hood*

Paul Bunyan's Christmas

By Taggert Ted Brown

CHRISTMAS must be properly observed even in his big rough-and-tumble logging camp, so decided Paul Bunyan, the famous Big Boss of many an old-time timber-cutting in the Wisconsin North Woods. He must have a real Christmas celebration for his lumberjacks. Paul had two thousand men in his camp on the Big Onion River that winter.

The day before Christmas, so says one of the old river yarns, Paul shouldered his huge ax and strode forth into the woods to pick a suitable Christmas tree. With him went his favorite oxen, Babe and Benny. All three tramped through the pines toward the Pyramid Forty. Now the Pyramid Forty was forty acres of land shaped like a pyramid, with a heavy forest of timber on all its sides. It was so high that to see to its top "took a week." It was "as far as twenty men could see." Several lumberjacks became permanently blind in just trying to see halfway up.

Paul Bunyan and his crew labored all one winter in trying to clear this forty. From it they cut one hundred million feet of lumber. Some of the men got one short leg from working all winter on one side of the slope. When they finally reached the top of the pyramid, the stumps at the bottom had already sprouted and shot up young trees seventy feet in height. When Paul Bunyan at last logged off this forty he hitched his oxen to it, dragged it to Lake Superior, and sunk the pyramid in its water. Geologists will probably never find any trace of it.

Well, on the very crest of the Pyramid Forty, Paul found just the big pine that he wanted. With one mighty blow he felled this woodland giant. The oxen hauled it down the steep slope to camp.

With the tree over his shoulder Paul waded out into the very center of Pea Soup Lake and there set it up. It was a cold day and the water immediately froze about its butt and held it fast.

Incidentally, you have no idea what a remarkable lake Pea Soup Lake was. Its history goes something like this. One of Paul's teamsters was one day driving across this frozen lake with a load of peas when the ice suddenly crashed, drowning the oxen and spilling the peas into the water. It was a sad loss, for the peas were badly needed. But Paul arose to the occasion. He dammed up the lake outlet and fired the slashings which he had caused to be piled around the shore. Joe, the cook, threw in a quantity of salt and pepper. So Paul boiled the water in the lake and the camp had good pea soup with an oxtail flavor all winter. When the men were cutting timber at a distance, Joe's assistants got the soup out to them by freezing it into sticks and pieces of rope. Some of the men drilled holes in their ax handles and filled these with soup. Their hands on the ax handles kept it warm until required for food.

After Paul had set the tree in Pea Soup Lake, it froze upright and solid. The great fir towered above all the surrounding scenery. Paul now summoned all his handy men. With the help of Joe Muffraw, the camp cook; his camp foreman, Black Dan McDonald; and several lumberjacks, Bunyan set to work to decorate the tree properly. Muffraw and his colored assistants brought along, from the big cook shanty, three logging sleds loaded to their tops with choice hams. These Paul had decided to substitute for candles to

illuminate the Christmas tree. Jim Liverpool, one of the lumber-jacks, was a famous jumper who had once cleared Lake Superior in three and a half jumps, winning a Congressional medal for his great feat. Paul ordered him to jump into the tree and hang the hams from the limbs. Black Dan, the foreman, assisted Jim, and Paul tossed the hams to them with sweeps of his mighty arm. A few of the hams they failed to catch, and greasy spots on the landscape of some northern counties showed where these fell.

These men set to work hanging the hams in the early morning. So numerous were the branches and so thick the foliage of the tree that two of Muffraw's helpers got lost, when they went up with the men's lunch at noon. Joe had to send two of his big trained chipmunks to trail them. One never was found. Joe had fed these chipmunks on prune stones thrown out from the kitchen, and they had grown as big and fierce as tigers.

Big Ole, the camp blacksmith, was busy most of the morning with his sledge and punch, punching holes in the doughnuts which were to be hung on the tree. Iron balls were painted a red color to represent cherries, or gilded to look like oranges. These weighed twenty pounds apiece. A huge silvered ox-shoe was hung on the tip of the tree.

Paul ordered ten thousand popcorn balls to be suspended from his Christmas tree. It was the duty of Joe Muffraw to fill this large order, and Joe undertook the job without a whimper. He hit on the scheme of setting fire to three forties of timber slashings, and then throwing forty tons of shelled corn on the hot ashes. The noise of the popping corn was deafening. When it was all popped, Joe had old Brimstone Bill drive out the big oxen, Babe and Benny. Babe kicked the popcorn into balls. Benny rolled them past Joe and his assistants, who shoveled molasses over the huge spheres as they went by. These popcorn balls were simply thrown into the tree and stuck on its branches where they hit. At these points some were unrolled to make popcorn strings and garlands, and these were draped from limb to limb.

It was a hustle and bustle all day long to get that big tree dressed for the celebration. Some of the lumberjacks got pretty well tired out. Hels Helson, the Big Swede, fell asleep under its branches. Babe, the Big Blue Ox, mistook his blonde head of hair for a bale of hay and ate it nearly bald before he awoke.

On Christmas Eve, the light from the thousand blazing hams on Paul Bunyan's tree was seen for two hundred miles away. That night two thousand lumberjacks from Paul's Big Onion camp gathered on the ice about the big tree. It was time for merriment and rejoicing. French Pete brought his company of fiddlers and accordion and harmonica players. The singing, dancing, and horseplay lasted for an entire week. No one thought of retiring to the bunkhouses. The big celebration might have lasted longer but the hams on the tree finally burned out.

Of the lumberjacks who worked for Paul that memorable winter, none will ever forget the Christmas tree on the Big Onion.